SCIENCE ON TRIAL

Also by Dr Robert Sharpe

The Cruel Deception - the use of animals in medical research (Thorsons, 1988).

SCIENCE ON TRIAL

The Human Cost of Animal Experiments

Dr Robert Sharpe

Awareness Publishing Limited

First published 1994

British Library Cataloguing in Publication Data.
A catalogue record for this book is available from the British Library.

ISBN 0 9523069 0 5
Published by Awareness Publishing Ltd., PO Box No. 533 Sheffield S11 9YU, England.

Printed in Great Britain by ALD Ltd., Sheffield, South Yorkshire.

to Stavely.

" The public in America has been kept in the dark, even more than the public in England, about this matter of vivisection.... The 'sentimentality' in this matter is to be found, not in those who oppose this monstrous crime, but in the ridiculous awe with which the average person, hypnotized by these crafty scientists and their sycophantic press, regard the whole problem. What science is really suggesting is that it is a sign of superior intellect to be completely devoid of natural goodness, of natural pity, and of all natural sensitiveness."

John Cowper Powys 1872-1963

CONTENTS

*101 documented examples of
failures,fatalities, misleading
results, mistakes and missed
opportunities which have occurred
through our acceptance of
vivisection.*

ACKNOWLEDGMENTS

This book is a product of determination and I should like to thank those who have assisted in differing ways to overcome many and varied obstacles: Animal Aid, The American Anti-Vivisection Society, The British Union for the Abolition of Vivisection, The International Association Against Painful Experiments on Animals, Annabel Holt, Sir John Gielgud, Lorraine Kay, Joanna Lumley, John McArdle, Mike Parr, Jose Parry and Colin Smith.

FOREWORD

I long ago came to the conclusion that it was horribly evil to experiment on other living beings and then attempt to justify the practice by calling it 'medical research'. This was but my natural reaction when I learnt of the suffering inflicted on animals by supposedly educated and 'ethical' men - men who regarded animals not as feeling creatures but as mere tools to a trade.

I have not been alone with my feelings. In past times an exalted cast of opposition spoke out against vivisection including Queen Victoria, Mahatma Ghandi, Voltaire, Samuel Johnson, Lord Shaftesbury, Victor Hugo, John Ruskin, Robert Browning, Richard Wagner, Charles Dickens, CG Jung, Dr Albert Schweitzer, CS Lewis and George Bernard Shaw. Today a host of celebrity voices join with the thousands of lesser known individuals who tirelessly work to free laboratory animals from the yoke of suffering.

Animal experiments, it is sometimes claimed, have been responsible for virtually every medical discovery in recorded history. Such propaganda tells us that we need animal experiments if we are to find cures to mankind's ills. Yet for all the suffering and resources used we don't seem to be very much better off. Always it is the apparent medical triumphs which make headline news. "Breakthroughs", invariably around an invisible corner, rarely,if ever, arrive. Disasters, such as unforeseen fatal drug side effects, are never connected to the 'safety' testing methods which delivered them into our hands. Consequently,the failure of animal research does not, to our shame, make the headline news it should.

I am only able to say with any certainty that vivisection is an appalling practice that should be stopped immediately. My knowledge does not extend to the point where it supports my inner certainty that it is also a mistake, a calamatous error which mankind as a whole has yet to wake up to.

Dr Sharpe's book adds fuel to the 'gut' reaction one has against animal experimentation. There is little doubt that the public needs to be made aware of the errors being committed in its collective name. The eminent writer John Galsworthy said of vivisection, "When a thing exists which you really abhor, I wish you would remember a little whether in letting it alone you are minding your own business on principle, or simply because it is comfortable to do so."

We need to extend our knowledge of this subject and not be in awe of those who seek to diminish the concerns of ordinary people who have retained the ability to know right from wrong. And one day, I pray soon, if enough people clamour for the better, humane sciences presently being side-lined as second-best 'alternatives', the dreadful mistake of vivisection may yet be rectified.

John Gielgud

INTRODUCTION

In 1962 scientists at the University of Oklahoma described the effects of LSD on a male elephant called Tusko. They were attempting to induce "musth", a natural condition in which elephants periodically become violent and uncontrollable. The dose of LSD was calculated from the amount that puts cats into a rage, adjustment being made for the elephant's greater body weight. At 8.00am on August 3, Tusko received his injection but the dose proved too large. Tusko immediately began trumpeting and rushing around the pen, then he stopped and swayed, finding it increasingly difficult to stay upright. His mate Judy tried to support him but Tusko collapsed, defecated and went into convulsions. Within 2 hours he was dead. The scientists concluded that elephants are particularly sensitive to LSD.[1]

It may be hard to believe that scientists carry out such experiments but the *result*, that one animal is more susceptible than another, would come as no surprise to veterinarians. Knowledge of differences between the species is crucial in veterinary practice since animals often vary in their response to drugs, poisons and disease.

There are many examples. Although dichlorvos is safely used to treat intestinal worms in the horse, it can poison poultry.[2] In contrast, sodium monensin controls parasites in broiler chickens but is lethal to horses.[2] Aspirin poisons cats, as do phenol-based disinfectants;[3] rabbits can eat freely the leaves of the deadly nightshade;[4] horses suffer brain disease if they eat yellow star thistle, a weed found in the Southern United States, although other animals are not affected;[2] rats, rabbits and mice are physiologically unable to vomit;[3] the intestinal treatment haloxon is 100 times more toxic to geese than to hens;[2] rats are hardly affected by TB;[4] and unlike guinea pigs, cats and dogs do not need vitamin C in their diet.[5] As one veterinarian explains, "it is unwise to extrapolate information concerning drugs from one species to another."[3]

It might be thought that similar, common-sense conclusions would apply to human medicine. After all, knowledge can be gained through human population studies, clinical observation of patients who are ill or who have died, work with healthy volunteers, test-tube experiments with human tissues, and computer simulations programmed with data from patients, all of which are directly relevant to people. In fact millions of animals suffer and die as human surrogates, and America's National Institutes of Health spends more on research with animals than on investigations of our own species![6] It is as if the problems caused by species variation have conveniently disappeared, since they are rarely mentioned by animal research advocates in their propaganda.

It is easy to understand why the issue is ignored or avoided. In the heated debate surrounding animal experiments, an admission that results may only be relevant to the species under test would destroy the pretence that vivisection is vital to our health, or that all medical advances require animals. Yet the hundred or so examples described here show that, on the contrary, animal research can be dangerously misleading.

It might still be argued that these are only isolated cases and that most animal experiments correctly predict human responses. Perhaps surprisingly, few major comparative studies have been carried out [7] but an analysis of drug side-effects by Ralph Heywood, former Director of Britain's Huntingdon Research Centre, found only a 5-25% correlation between harmful effects in people and the results of animal experiments.[8] This confirms the view of Dr Kenneth

Melmon of the Cardiovascular Research Institute, University of California, that "In most cases, the animal tests cannot predict what will happen when the drug is given to man."[9]

Some side-effects are better predicted than others.[7] A review of 45 drugs by Britain's Committee on Safety of Medicines found that animal experiments were most likely to predict vomitting and gastrointestinal disturbances. Overall, however, the survey found that, at best, just 25% of the toxic effects observed in animal tests actually occurred in people.[10]

An especially controversial area is the use of animals to identify cancer-causing chemicals. In 1983 the pharmaceutical company Pfizer carried out a special study to test the efficiency of animal tests. The results would be vitally important because despite costing millions of dollars, no one really knew whether they provided adequate protection against hazardous substances.[11] Human findings were compared with experimental data from rats and mice for all chemicals known to cause cancer in people. The outcome was disturbing: in most cases animal tests had given the wrong answer. The report concluded that we would have been better off to toss a coin! [12]

Subsequent reports, however, suggest that when tested "adequately", nearly all human carcinogens have, eventually, been shown to cause cancer in some species of animal. But this is misleading: if substances like asbestos, tobacco, arsenic, benzene, alcohol and soot were not *already suspected of causing cancer in people*, scientists would never have persisted with attempts to induce the disease in animals. Reliance would have been placed on one or two routine feeding or inhalation tests to which new chemicals are now submitted. Since all the first animal tests for the above-named substances proved negative,[13] some of the most dangerous human carcinogens would have been deemed safe.

Misgivings over the validity of animal research also apply to the study of disease. After analysing 10 randomly chosen "animal models" of human illness, the Medical Research Modernization Committee found little, if any, contribution towards the treatment of patients.[14] They discovered, for instance, that chemically-induced cancer of the colon in rats was not relevant to our understanding, diagnosis and treatment of human colon cancer.

Obviously there are times when people and animals respond in a similar way, although this is never known until *after* human studies have taken place. The problem is that artificially induced disease in animals is never identical to the naturally arising disorder in patients, making animal research a logically flawed process.[15] Furthermore, the differences in body chemistry between species can be so great that one well-known drug researcher states "...it is often a matter of pure luck that animal experiments lead to clinically useful drugs."[16]

In the scientific journals at least, some animal researchers recognise that species differences limit the value of their experiments. David Galloway of Glasgow's Western Infirmary concedes that "the ultimate dilemma with any animal model of human disease is that it can never reflect the human situation with complete accuracy."[17] Nevertheless, experimenters insist they are still able to generate insights and, focussing on cancer of the colon, Galloway argues that "The lack of a single animal model which closely parallels the human disease need not be regarded as a major disadvantage."

Tragically, vivisection is so ingrained that entirely new strains or species are being developed in an elusive search for the ideal animal model. Using the techniques of genetic engineering, scientists can alter an animal's genetic make-up, producing creatures that are designed to suffer and die in medical research. The unfortunate "oncomouse", produced by inserting human cancer genes into the embryos of mice, quickly develops cancer and dies within 90 days. In other cases researchers have introduced similar genetic defects to those found in sick people.

Although experimenters hope that genetically engineered animals will more accurately mimic human disease, "...quite often the model does not resemble the corresponding human condition as closely as might be expected." [18] In the case of Waadernburg's syndrome type 1, a genetic disorder in which loss of hearing is a common feature, the genetically engineered mice do not become deaf.[18] Another example is "cystic fibrosis mice".

Discovery of the cystic fibrosis gene in human sufferers led vivisectors to disrupt a similar gene in mice. The animals become ill and die within 40 days but although hailed as a major breakthrough, there are differences from the disease in people:[19] most importantly the animal's lungs do not become infected or blocked with mucus as they do in human patients yet it is lung infections that kill 95% of people with cystic fibrosis.

A further case is the use of transgenic mice in AIDS research. In an attempt to make mice susceptible to the disease, the genetic material which produces HIV was inserted into their tissues. Again, the animals do become ill but their immune system is not suppressed as it is in people with AIDS.[20]

Whatever animal research may have contributed in the past, this is no reason for uncritical acceptance of the method for all time. Moral values change and the mediaeval idea that lives can only be saved by sacrificing animals is no longer acceptable. These ethical objections are strongly reinforced by scientific arguments since the physiological and biochemical differences between people and animals stress the urgent need for a more reliable approach: it is in *all* our interests to challenge animal experiments.

If there is to be a more enlightened future, pressure for reform must be combined with a new generation of scientists who no longer regard animals as the disposable tools of research.

References

1) L.J.West et al, *Science*, 1962, December 7, 1100-1103.
2) E.G.C.Clarke,*The Veterinary Record*, 1976, March 13, 215-218.
3) L.E.Davis, *Journal of the American Veterinary Medical Associations*, 1979, vol.175, 1014-1015.
4) G.Macpherson (Ed.), *Black's Medical Dictionary*, 37th edition (Adam & Charles Black, 1992).
5) T.Koppanyi & M.Avery, *Clinical Pharmacology & Therapeutics*, 1966, vol.7, 250-270.
6) *Alternatives to Animal Use in Research, Testing & Education*, U.S. Congress, Office of Technology Assessment, 1986.
7) R.Heywood in *Animals & Alternatives in Toxicity Testing*, Eds. M.Balls et al (Academic Press, 1983).
8) R.Heywood in *Animal Toxicity studies: Their Relevance for Man*, Eds. C.E.Lumley & S.R.Walker (Quay Publishing,1990).
9) K.L.Melmon, *Clinical Pharmacology & Therapeutics*, 1976, vol.20, 125-129.
10) A.P.Fletcher, *Journal of the Royal Society of Medicine*, 1978, vol.71, 693-696.
11) Editorial, *Journal of Pharmaceutical Sciences*, 1980, vol.69, number 2.
12) D.Salsburg, *Fundamental & Applied Toxicology*, 1983, vol.3, 63-67.
13) see under chemical names in text.
14) S.R.Kaufman et al, *Perspectives in Animal Research*, 1989, vol.1, Supplement.
15) *A Critical Look at Animal Research*, Medical Research Modernization Committee (New York, 1990).
16) B.Brodie, *Pharmacologist*, 1964, vol.6, 12-26.
17) D.Galloway, *Cancer Surveys*, 1989, vol.8, 169-188.
18) K.Davies, *Nature*, 1992, September 3, 86; see also P.Parham, *Nature*, 1991, October 10, 503-505.
19) Editorial, *Lancet*, 1992, September 19, 702-703.
20) M.B.Gardner & P.A.Luciw, *The Faseb Journal*, 1989, vol.3, 2593-2606.

THE EVIDENCE

TRANSPLANT DRUG ALMOST LOST

The life-saving qualities of a new anti-rejection drug, FK506, could have been missed when animal experiments suggested it was too toxic for human use.[1] The tests were carried out at Cambridge University in England and showed that "...animal toxicity was too severe to proceed to clinical trial".[2] US researchers, however, decided it was worthy of further investigation but nevertheless did not feel justified in first giving the drug to healthy volunteers, the usual practice in drug development, since this could be "potentially dangerous."[3] Instead, FK506 was administered as a last chance option to liver transplant patients in "desperate plight". So far clinical experience with FK506 has been very promising.[4]

Animal tests also proved misleading in suggesting that FK506 would give better results if combined with another antirejection drug, cyclosporin. However, clinical trials revealed the opposite, with FK506 actually *increasing* the kidney damage caused by cyclosporin.[3]

References

1) R.Allison, *Journal of the American Medical Association*, 1990, April 4, 1766.
2) R.Y.Calne et al, *Lancet*, 1989, July 22, 227.
3) T.E.Starzl et al, *Lancet*, 1989, October 28, 1000-1004.
4)J.Neuberger, *Hepatology*, 1991, vol.13, 1259-1260.

LEUKEMIA & THE NUCLEAR INDUSTRY

In 1983 a television documentary programme drew attention to an increased number of childhood leukemia cases in the vicinity of the nuclear reprocessing plant at Sellafield in Britain. Although the incidence of leukemia was 10 times the national average, the official Committee of Inquiry decided the nuclear facility was not the cause. Their conclusions were based on calculations from animal experiments. By preferring animal data to direct human observations, the effect was to minimise the risks of radiation.[1]

Subsequently, a major investigation concluded that radiation was indeed to blame, for those at highest risk of leukemia were born to fathers who worked at the nuclear plant.[2] Not all studies supported these findings and clarification must await further epidemiological research. Nevertheless, the observations linking leukemia clusters to nuclear plants did persuade the Ministry of Defence and the government's Health and Safety Executive to recommend major cuts in the maximum radiation doses to which workers are legally exposed.[3]

References

1) E.Millstone in *Animal Experimentation: The Consensus Changes*, Ed. G.Langley (MacMillan, 1989)
2) M.J.Gardner et al, *British Medical Journal*, 1990, February 17, 423-429.
3) *The Guardian*, 1991, March 22 and April 30.

MIGRAINE PILL'S HORRIFIC SIDE EFFECT

The *British National Formulary* (1993) warns that methysergide, a treatment for migraine, should only be administered under hospital supervision because of dangerous side-effects resulting from abnormal formation of fibrous tissue. This condition, known medically as retroperitoneal fibrosis, can lead to obstruction of abdominal blood vessels and blockage of the tube carrying urine from the kidneys to the bladder. Fibrotic damage to the heart valves has also been reported and can result in heart failure.

Methysergide's life-threatening side-effects were not predicted by animal tests,[1] nor could they be induced during subsequent experimentation, and a report in the *British Medical Journal* notes that "Attempts to reproduce these fibrotic lesions in animals have been unsuccessful."[2]

References

1) R.Heywood in *Animal Toxicity Studies: Their Relevance for Man*, Eds. C.E. Lumley & S.R.Walker (Quay Publications, 1990).
2) K.A.Misch, *British Medical Journal*, 1974, May 18, 365-366.

SUPROFEN JOINS BANNED LIST

The arthritis drug suprofen (Suprol) was withdrawn worldwide in May 1987 following reports of kidney problems and pain in the side of the body.[1] Patients experiencing these side-effects had to have their kidney function monitored for 2 years after they stopped taking the drug.[2] The dangers were unexpected because "In animal studies suprofen has been shown to have an excellent safety profile. No significant effects were observed on cardiac, renal [kidney] or central nervous system parameters in several species."[3]

References

1) *Drug Withdrawal from Sale*, C.Spriet-Pourra & M.Auriche (PJB Publications, 1988)
2) *FDA Drug Review: Postapproval Risks 1976-1985* (US General Accounting Office, April 1990).
3) A.Yeadon et al, *Pharmacology*, 1983, vol.27, Suppl.1, 87-94.

ANIMALS MIX DEADLY COCKTAIL OF CONFUSING RESULTS

For centuries, alcohol has been regarded as poisonous for the liver.[1] That is, until the first half of the 20th century when it was cleared of liver toxicity following experiments on animals.[1,2] In 1934, a summary of animal tests concluded that "experimental evidence has not substantiated the belief that alcohol is a direct cause of cirrhosis."[3] Based largely on experiments with rats, researchers later argued that "there is no more evidence of a specific toxic effect of pure ethyl alcohol upon liver cells than there is for one due to sugar."[4] Today, alcohol is once again considered a liver toxin but since it has proved so difficult to induce cirrhosis in laboratory animals, there are still some who doubt the evidence.[5]

Animal experiments have proved misleading in other areas of alcohol research. Although it has been known for decades that too much alcohol can cause cancer, this well established clinical fact has been questioned because it proved impossible to induce the disease in animals. Indeed, some insist that alcohol should not be classified as a human carcinogen since there is no evidence from animal experiments![6]

Alcohol seems more toxic to the circulatory system of humans than animals, and whereas prolonged consumption raises the blood pressure in alcoholics, this is not usually the case in rats.[7] And whilst alcohol can damage the human heart, "Studies on a variety of animals being given large amounts of ethanol [alcohol] over long periods of time did not lead to heart failure. Also, until recently when the heart of the Nicholas turkey was shown to be susceptible to alcoholic damage, there has been no animal model of alcoholic cardiomyopathy [heart muscle damage] as it is seen in man."[7]

During the early 1970s researchers described how alcohol could induce physical dependence in mice. The experiments showed that the tranquillizing drug Librium could reduce the severity of withdrawal convulsions, but also suggested that the treatment had a lethal side-effect with some of the animals dying.[8] Fortunately, clinical studies carried out 6 years earlier had already shown that Librium was effective [9] and the drug remains an important treatment for alcohol withdrawal symptoms.

Despite the known effects of alcohol and the availability of human tissues to supplement clinical observations, there seems no shortage of funds for animal experiments. A report by the National Research Information Centre, compiled by Murry Cohen MD and Constance Young, revealed that the US Government funded 284 alcohol research projects involving animals during 1986, costing nearly $24 million. [10] "Animal research", they concluded, "has had no significant effect on our knowledge of alcohol-use disorders."

References

1) H.J.Zimmerman, *Alcoholism: Clinical & Experimental Research,* 1986, vol.10, 3-15.
2) C.S.Lieber & L.M.DeCarli, *Journal of Hepatology,* 1991, vol.12, 394-401.
3) V.H.Moon, *Archives of Pathology,* 1934, vol.18, 381-424.
4) Reported in Ref.2.
5) R.F.Derr et al, *Journal of Hepatology,* 1990, vol.10, 381-386.
6) L.Tomatis et al, *Japanese Journal of Cancer Research,* 1989, vol.80, 795-807.
7) J.V.Jones et al, *Journal of Hypertension,* 1988, vol.6, 419-422.
8) D.B.Goldstein, *Journal of Pharmacology & Experimental Therapeutics,* 1972, vol.183, 14-22.
9) G.Sereny & H.Kalant, *British Medical Journal,* 1965, January 9, 92-97.
10) M.Cohen & C.Young, *Alcoholic Rats,* The National Research Information Centre, 1989.

PESTICIDE POISONINGS

In February 1986 the British Parliament's Agriculture Committee began an enquiry into pesticides and human health. The Committee learnt that great reliance is placed on animal experiments but that "...similar tests in different animal species often yield quite different results."[1] An example is the organophosphate pesticide dipterex which produces nerve damage in people but not in the animal tests specially designed to detect such injuries.[2] In fact, Dr Murray of the National Poisons Unit informed the Committee that *one* well documented case of human poisoning is equivalent to 20,000 animal experiments![1]

The Committee concluded that "It cannot be satisfactory to rely on animals so much as a means of testing and, as other forms of testing become available, we recommend that they be adopted...we are satisfied from the evidence that we have received that animal testing can produce misleading results."[1]

References

1) Special Report of the House of Commons Agriculture Committee, reproduced in *FRAME News*, 1987, No.16, p.2.
2) A.N.Worden in *Animals and Alternatives in Toxicity Testing*, Eds. M.Balls et al (Academic Press, 1983).

ARSENIC AND THE DECADES OF FAILURE

It was fortunate that so much *human* evidence linked arsenic to cancer because for over 70 years, researchers were unable to "confirm" the dangers in laboratory animals. Suspicions that arsenic might cause cancer date back to 1809 when its harmful effects in drinking water were first noted.[1] In 1887/88, Sir Jonathon Hutchinson described the earliest cases of cancer resulting from medicinal use of arsenic[1] and subsequently, others have reported cancers in chemical, agricultural and metallurgical workers exposed to arsenic.[2]

Animal tests began in 1911 and an historical analysis of the subject, published during 1947, described how dozens of experiments had been performed.[1] However, these had given "only doubtful results." The tests continued but still proved negative, and in 1969 researchers at America's National Cancer Institute stated that "arsenic has been suspected by many investigators as a carcinogen in man, though there is no supporting evidence from animal experiments."[3] And in 1977 a further summary of the data concluded that "there is little evidence that arsenic compounds are carcinogenic in experimental animals."[2]

Finally, in the late 1980s, scientists managed to produce cancer in animals. This was 180 years after arsenic was first suggested as a human carcinogen. Despite decades of failure, animal researchers had at least been correct about one thing: in 1962 Heuper and Payne wrote that "With perseverance and some luck arsenicals one day may be shown to cause cancer in animals."[4]

References
1) O.Neubauer, *British Journal of Cancer*, 1947, vol.1, 192-251.
2) F.W.Sunderman Jr. in *Advances in Modern Toxicology*, vol.2, Eds, R.A.Goyer & M.A.Mehlman (Wiley, 1977).
3) A.M.Lee & J.F.Fraumeni Jr. *Journal of the National Cancer Institute*, 1969, vol.42, 1045-1052.
4) W.C.Heuper & W.W.Payne, *Archives of Environmental Health*, 1962, vol.5, 459.

RODENT TESTS MISS INDUSTRIAL CANCER RISK

Benzene is used as a starting point for the production of industrial chemicals and for the manufacture of detergents, explosives and pharmaceuticals. It is also present in gasoline and was once commonly employed as a chemical solvent. Because benzene is so widely used, there has been considerable debate over the safety of exposed workers, especially since experience has shown it to be a cancer hazard.

Tragically, human evidence was once again undermined by the animal laboratory. According to Lester Lave of the Brookings Institute in Washington DC, "although there are reliable human data linking benzene to leukemia, scientists have been reluctant to categorise benzene as a carcinogen because there are no published reports that it induces leukemia in rodents."[1]

In fact, *14* separate animal trials, starting in 1932, failed to show that benzene caused cancer.[2] Only during the late 1980s were researchers finally able to induce cancer in laboratory animals by dosing them with benzene.

References

1) L.B.Lave, *The American Statistician*, 1982, vol.36, 260-261.
2) D.M.De Marini et al, in *Benchmarks: Alternative Methods in Toxicology*, Ed. M.A.Mehlman (Princeton Scientific Publishing Co.Inc.,1989).

VALUABLE EYE THERAPY WOULD NOT PASS RABBIT TEST

Chymotrypsin is widely used in ophthalmic surgery for the treatment of cataract. Although recommended for human use,[1] chymotrypsin is harmful to the rabbit eye. In his book *Toxicology of the Eye* (1974), Morton Grant states that "the rabbit cornea appears to differ significantly from the human cornea in its reaction to α-chymotrypsin. It has been noted repeatedly that introduction of α-chymotrypsin into the [rabbit's] corneal stroma...leads to severe swelling reaction of cornea, much more than is seen in human beings, and in some instances leading to perforation of the cornea."

Reference

1) *British National Formulary*, No.26(BMA and The Royal Pharmaceutical Society of G.B., 1993).

RABBIT TEST MISSES HUMAN EYE IRRITANT

Lindane is probably best known as an agricultural insecticide but very dilute lotions, creams and shampoos are used therapeutically for treating lice and scabies. Nevertheless such preparations can cause "excessive eye irritation" and conjunctivitis,[1] and the *British National Formulary* (1993) warns users to "avoid contact with eyes". In rabbits, however, application of a far more concentrated solution produced only minimal effects.[1] Furthermore, exposure to lindane in the form of a dust proved non-irritating to the eyes and nasal mucosa of rabbits but caused irritation to the eyes and respiratory passages of sensitive people.[1]

Reference

1) W.M.Grant, *Toxicology of the Eye,* 2nd edition (Charles Thomas, 1974).

SLIMMING TREATMENT CAUSED CATARACTS

In 1933, following "thorough" experiments on animals, researchers described the use of dinitrophenol as a treatment for obesity. However, doctors soon noticed that the drug unexpectedly caused cataracts in some of their patients, and nearly 200 cases were reported before the drug was prohibited for internal use. Attempts were made to replicate the clinical findings in rats, rabbits, guinea pigs and dogs but none of the experiments produced any change in the lens of the eye.[1] In 1942, a summary of the tests stated that "All attempts to produce experimental cataracts in laboratory animals by various and repeated doses of dinitrophenol have been unsuccessful."[2]

Although birds are rarely used for the safety testing of drugs, later experiments accidentally discovered that cataracts could be induced in chicks dosed with dinitrophenol in their food.[1]

Similar problems were encountered with triparanol (Mer-29), a drug used to lower cholesterol levels. The cataracts observed in human patients could be induced in rats and dogs after very high doses but not in rabbits and monkeys.[3] Triparanol was withdrawn in 1962.

References
1) B.H.Robbins, *Journal of Pharmacology*, 1944, vol.80, 264-269.
2) Reproduced in ref.1.
3) W.M.Grant, *Toxicology of the Eye*, 2nd edition (Charles Thomas, 1974).

SHOCK TREATMENT

For years, high doses of corticosteroids have been recommended for the treatment of septic shock, a condition which leads to heart, kidney and respiratory failure in a high proportion of patients. The idea was based on animal experiments where corticosteroids improve survival when given before shock [1] or shortly afterwards.[2]

It has been pointed out, however, that "...extrapolation of data from experimental models of shock to the clinical setting may be dangerous and misleading."[3] So it is not surprising that an analysis of clinical trials by the *Drug & Therapeutics Bulletin* found that "high-dose corticosteroids are ineffective for the prevention or treatment of shock associated with sepsis. They do not improve outcome, and make secondary infection worse. They may harm patients with impaired renal [kidney] function."[1] For instance, one trial found that corticosteroids not only failed to prevent or reverse shock but actually seemed to *increase* deaths amongst patients, even though treatment was initiated within 2 hours.[4]

References

1) *Drug & Therapeutics Bulletin*, 1990, vol.28, 74-75.
2) S.G.Hershey in *Anaesthesiology: Proceedings of the VI World Congress of Anaesthesiology*, Mexico City, April 1976, Eds. E.Hulsz et al (Excerpta Medica, 1977).
3) A.S.Nies in *Clinical Pharmacology: Basic Principles in Therapeutics*, Eds. K.L.Melmon & H.F.Morrelli (MacMillan,1978)
4) R.C.Bone et al, *New England Journal of Medicine*, 1987, September 10, 653-658.

BODY CHEMICALS PRODUCE OPPOSITE EFFECTS IN ANIMALS

An important area of medical research is pharmacology where scientists study exactly how drugs and natural body substances exert their effects on the tissues. An understanding of the chemical processes involved can be valuable in providing a more rational basis for the design of new treatments. Unfortunately, many pharmacologists rely on animals despite numerous contradictory results. As a result of experiments with dogs, acetylcholine, a chemical produced by nerve endings, was widely believed to dilate the coronary arteries. But in human coronary tissue it causes a narrowing of the vessels which is thought to lead to heart spasm in a living person.[1] Another body chemical, bradykinin, relaxes blood vessels in human brain tissue but contracts them in dogs.[2]

Further species differences have been found with the leukotrienes (LT), natural substances involved in inflammation. Leukotrienes known as LTC4 and LTD4 constrict blood vessels in the guinea pig's skin but dilate corresponding tissues from people and pigs.[3] Yet another case is the prostaglandins (PG), a family of substances discovered over 50 years ago in human seminal fluid: in heart tissue from cats and rabbits, PGE1 has no effect on contractile force or heart rate but increases them in rats, guinea pigs and chickens.[4]

Some pharmacologists have recognised that "direct extrapolation from animals to humans is frequently invalid," so that "recently much interest has focussed on use of human autopsy or biopsy tissue as a means of overcoming these limitations."[5]

References

1) S.Kalsner, *Journal of Physiology,* 1985, vol.358, 509-526.
2) K.Schror & R.Verheggen, *Trends in Pharmacological Sciences,* 1988, vol.9, 71-74.
3) P.J.Piper et al, *Annals of the New York Academy of Sciences,* 1988, vol.524, 133-141.
4) S.Bergstrom et al, *Pharmacological Reviews,* 1968, vol.20, 1-48.
5) *Trends in Pharmacological Sciences,* 1987, vol.8, 289-290.

BLOOD PRESSURE PILL LEADS TO WITHDRAWAL SYNDROME

During the 1960s animal experiments suggested that clonidine might be a useful drug for preventing migraine.[1] Using cats, experimenters found that clonidine interfered with physiological processes thought to cause headaches. The drug was introduced in 1969 but clinical experience now suggests that clonidine is largely ineffective and little better than a dummy pill.[1]

Clonidine proved more successful in the treatment of high blood pressure. Its ability to lower blood pressure was discovered accidentally when it was given to people as a nasal decongestant.[2] Although effective, there were serious unexpected side-effects when patients stopped taking the drug: the "clonidine withdrawal syndrome" is characterised in extreme cases by sweating, trembling, rapid heart beat and a dangerous rise in blood pressure. The symptoms may occur after only one or two missed doses or even after gradual withdrawal over 3 days.

Attempts to replicate the condition in dogs and cats produced inconsistent results [3] whilst in the rat "..attempts to reproduce the clonidine discontinuation syndrome...have met with even more difficulties and controversy than those encountered in dogs and cats."[4] 'Success' was only achieved when researchers implanted a special pump into the rat's body to maintain adequate levels of clonidine in the bloodstream prior to withdrawal.[4]

In view of its serious side-effects, the *Drug and Therapeutics Bulletin* considers clonidine obsolete for the treatment of high blood pressure.[5]

References
1) *Drug & Therapeutics Bulletin*, 1990, vol.28, 79-80.
2) A.S.Nies in *Clinical Pharmacology: Basic Principles in Therapeutics,* 2nd edition, Eds. K.L.Melmon & H.F.Morrelli (MacMillan, 1978).
3) L.Hansson et al, *American Heart Journal*, 1973, vol.85, 605-610.
4) M.J.M.C. Thoolen et al, *General Pharmacology*, 1981, vol.12, 303-308.
5) *Drug & Therapeutics Bulletin*, 1984, vol.22, 42-43.

DRUG INDUCED DISASTER LEAVES THOUSANDS DEAD

A major disaster occurred in the UK during the 1960s when at least 3,500 young asthma sufferers died following use of isoprenaline aerosol inhalers.[1] Fatalities were reported in countries using a particularly concentrated form of aerosol that delivered 0.4mg of isoprenaline per spray.[2,3] Fortunately, the death rate declined rapidly when the drug was made "prescription only" and warnings were issued to doctors.

Attempts to replicate the effects in laboratory animals proved difficult. In 1971 researchers at New York's Food and Drug Research Laboratory reported that "Intensive toxicologic studies with rats, guinea pigs, dogs and monkeys at dosage levels far in excess of current commercial metered dose vials... have not elicited similar adverse effects."[4]

Experimenters persisted in their attempts however, and eventually found that by artificially reducing the amount of oxygen in the animal's tissues, they could increase the toxic effects of isoprenaline on the heart.[5]

References

1) W.H.Inman in *Monitoring for Drug Safety*, Ed. W.H.Inman (MTP Press, 1980).
2) P.D.Stolley, *American Review of Respiratory Diseases*, 1972, vol.105, 883-890.
3) P.D. Stolley & R.Schinnar, *Lancet*, 1979, October 27, 896.
4) S.Carson et al, *Pharmacologist*, 1971, vol.18, 272.
5) *British Medical Journal*, 1972, November 25, 443-444.

ANIMAL TESTS CONFUSE PAINKILLER PROBE

Since 1953 when doctors first drew attention to the kidney damage associated with prolonged use of combination painkillers, there have been many animal experiments to try and clarify the effects seen in people.[1] In fact, these have only obscured the issue. For example, interest centered on which ingredient was responsible, and although suspicion naturally fell on phenacetin since this was present in most analgesic mixtures, the characteristic kidney damage seen in patients could not be reproduced in animals.[1]

The experiments also suggested that *aspirin* rather than phenacetin was to blame in painkillers containing the two drugs.[2] This is because, unlike phenacetin, aspirin readily induces kidney damage in laboratory animals. Eventually, *human* studies showed that phenacetin was indeed a major culprit.[3]

So contradictory were the experiments that a major analysis of the subject concluded that if doctors had not first observed the effects in patients, they would never have been suspected, foreseen or predicted by animal tests.[1] Phenacetin was finally withdrawn in 1980 when there were also suspicions that it caused cancer.

References

1) I.Rosner, *CRC Critical Reviews in Toxicology*, 1976, vol.4, 331-352.
2) *British Medical Journal*, 1970, October 17, 125-126.
3) K.G.Koutsaimanis & H.E. de Wardener, *British Medical Journal*, 1970, October 17, 131-134.

DIARRHOEA TREATMENT LEAVES 10,000 VICTIMS

During the 1960s, Japan suffered a devastating epidemic of drug-induced disease associated with clioquinol, the main ingredient of Ciba-Geigy's antidiarrhoea medicines Enterovioform and Mexaform. At least 10,000 people, and perhaps as many as 30,000, were victims of SMON (subacute myelo-optic neuropathy), a new disease whose symptoms include numbness, weakness in the legs, paralysis and eye problems, including blindness.[1] In 1970 Japan's Ministry of Health and Welfare banned the drug and 15 years later clioquinol was withdrawn worldwide.

Clioquinol's harmful effects result from nerve damage yet animal experiments performed by the company revealed "no evidence that clioquinol is neurotoxic", tests being carried out on rats, cats, beagles and rabbits.[2]

Although some argue that "Animal tests have consistently failed to reproduce the effects seen in humans,"[3] researchers at the Okayama University Medical School say they have induced clioquinol toxicity in mongrels.[4] Nevertheless, they note that different species respond differently, with monkeys, hens, cocks, and mice only mildly affected even after higher doses. They also found that beagle dogs were 3-4 times less sensitive to clioquinol than mongrels, and concluded that "These facts suggest strongly differences in strains as well as species of animals for the neurotoxicity of clioquinol."

References
1) *Lancet*, 1977, March 5, 534.
2) R.Hess et al, *Lancet*, 1972, August 26, 424-425.
3) W.Sneader, *Drug Development: From Laboratory to Clinic* (Wiley)
4) J.Tateishi et al, *Lancet*, 1972, June 10, 1289-1290.

WOMEN AT RISK FROM "PILL" SAFETY TESTS

Careful observation of women taking the pill has shown that the most serious side-effects are on the circulatory system: there is an increased risk of blood clots leading to heart attacks, strokes and lung diseases. By 1980, Britain's Committee on Safety of Medicines (CSM) had received reports of 404 deaths.[1] Further studies found that 1-5% of women taking the pill have raised blood pressure.

None of these problems had been identified by animal experiments.[2] Furthermore, in some species oral contraceptives produced the opposite effect, making it more difficult for the blood to clot![3] As Professor Briggs of Deakin University in Australia points out, "Many experimental toxicity studies have been conducted on contraceptive oestrogens, alone or in combination with progesterones. At multiples of the human dose no adverse effect on blood clotting was found in mice, rats, dogs or non-human primates. Indeed, far from accelerating blood coagulation, high doses of oestrogens in rats and dogs prolonged clotting times. There is therefore no appropriate animal model for the coagulation changes occurring in women using oral contraceptives."[4]

In 1972, the CSM described tests on over 13,000 animals which showed that very high doses of oral contraceptives cause cancer.[5] But the rats and mice used in these experiments were so susceptible to cancer that even those not dosed with the pill (the "control" animals) suffered high levels of disease: for instance, lung and liver tumours were found in 25% and 23% of control mice, and adrenal, pituitary and breast tumours were found in 26%, 30% and 99% of control rats. Under these circumstances, the *British Medical Journal* noted, "It is difficult to see how experiments on strains of animals so exceedingly liable to develop tumours of these various kinds can throw any useful light on the carcinogenicity of any compound for man."[5] The *Journal* believed the tests neither incriminated nor exonerated the pill and concluded that we would have to wait for the results of human studies.

The uncertainty of animal experiments has meant that, effectively, oral contraceptives have been tested by women themselves during long term use.

References

1) G.R.Venning, *British Medical Journal*, 1983, January 22, 289-292.
2) R.Heywood in *Animal Toxicity Studies: Their Relevance for Man*, Eds. C.E.Lumley & S.R.Walker (Quay Publishing, 1990).
3) R.Heywood & P.F.Wadsworth in *Pharmacology of Estrogens*, Ed. R.R.Chaudhury (Pergamon Press, 1981).
4) M.H.Briggs in *Biomedical Research Involving Animals*, Eds. Z.Bankowski & N.Howard-Jones (CIOMS, 1984).
5) *British Medical Journal*, 1972, October 28, 190.

'SAFE' ANTIBIOTIC'S FATAL FLAW

Animal experiments suggested that chloramphenicol was a very safe drug but clinical experience soon revealed serious side-effects making it no longer suitable for internal use, except for life-threatening infections such as typhoid fever. In France, chloramphenicol has been completely withdrawn.[1]

In 1952, physicians in Baltimore drew attention to chloramphenicol's effects on nerve cells in the body.[2] They described a patient who almost became blind and who suffered such severe pain in her feet that she could only walk with the aid of pain-killing narcotic drugs. She had been taking chloramphenicol for 5 months. This was the first of many cases of optical and peripheral neuritis caused by chloramphenicol yet animal experiments had shown the drug to be practically free of side-effects, even after prolonged administration.[2]

Even more seriously, the drug caused aplastic anaemia, an often fatal blood disease sometimes terminating in leukemia. Once again, the effect had not been predicted by animal tests, and the *British Medical Journal* records how chloramphenicol produced nothing worse than transient anaemia in dogs when given the drug for long periods by injection, and nothing at all when given orally.[3]

Today we know that chloramphenicol's deadly side-effect can be identified by test-tube studies with human bone marrow cells.[4]

References

1) C.Spriet-Pourra & M.Auriche, *Drug Withdrawal from Sale* (PJB Publications, 1988).
2) L.Wallenstein & J.Snyder, *Annals of Internal Medicine*, 1952, vol.36, 1526-1528.
3) *British Medical Journal*, 1952, July 19, 136-138.
4) G.M.L.Gyte & J.R.B.Williams, *ATLA*, 1985, vol.13, 38-47.

DOCTORS WARNED ABOUT HALOTHANE LIVER TOXICITY

Halothane was introduced into clinical practice in 1956 and immediately hailed as a great advance in anaesthesia. Unfortunately, the anaesthetic was soon found to harm the liver and within 5 years, at least 350 cases of "halothane hepatitis" had been recorded. The condition sometimes proves fatal and between 1964 and 1985, 180 British deaths were linked to the drug.[1]

The original animal tests had shown no evidence of liver damage,[2] and " early attempts to produce an animal model of halothane hepatitis proved disappointing," according to anaesthetists at Edinburgh's Royal Infirmary.[3] Nevertheless, there has been no shortage of experiments: since 1976 five "animal models" have been described though "their application to humans is of doubtful significance." [3]

By 1986, when Britain's Committee on Safety of Medicines strengthened the warnings of liver toxicity in human patients, [4] it was still not clear whether the same injuries could be induced in animals.[5]

References
1) *British Medical Journal*, 1986, April 5, 949.
2) *Anaesthesiology*, 1963, vol.24, 109-110.
3) D.C.Ray & G.B.Drummond, *British Journal of Anaesthesia*, 1991, vol.67, 84-99.
4) *Scrip*, 1987, October 2, 2.
5) C.E.Blogg, *British Medical Journal*, 1986, June 28, 1691-1692.

CANCER-PRONE MICE CONTRADICT HUMAN EXPERIENCE

Butadiene is an important intermediate in the production of synthetic rubber but causes cancer in the $B_6C_3F_1$ strain of laboratory mouse, an animal widely used to assess the risk of chemicals. Tumours have also been found in rats although the dose was very high.

Based on the experiments with $B_6C_3F_1$ mice, America's National Institute of Occupational Safety and Health (NIOSH) has classified butadiene as a carcinogen, estimating that exposure to 2 parts per million for 45 years would result in 597 cancers per 10,000 people. However, careful observation of butadiene plant workers employed since 1945, and exposed to much higher levels of the chemical, revealed no extra cancers. On the contrary, overall cancer deaths were considerably less than among the ordinary public.[1]

The NIOSH findings have been criticised since there are many differences between people and the cancer prone $B_6C_3F_1$ mouse. According to an editorial in the journal *Science*,[1] "with trillions of dollars, loss of competitiveness, and jobs at stake, a searching review of the risk assessment methodology of the regulatory agencies is overdue."

Reference

1) P.H.Abelson, *Science*, 1992, June 19, 1609.

VIVISECTION UNDERMINES MINERS' WELFARE

During the 20th century, there has been much debate over the actual cause of pneumoconiosis, a lung disease suffered by coal miners because of their occupation. For many years, scientists believed that inhalation of coal dust was "completely innocuous" and that any respiratory disease arose from the silica that sometimes contaminated the coal.[1] In bituminous coal pits, where there is little exposure to silica, mining was not considered dangerous and consequently few observational studies were carried out in the US between 1900 and 1960. As a result, there was almost no information on the amount of coal workers' pneumoconiosis until the Public Health Service conducted studies in 1962/63.[1]

The idea that coal dust was harmless originated primarily from the vivisection laboratory. According to an editorial in the *British Medical Journal*,[2] scientists who believed silica to be the responsible contaminant, "take their strongest stand on the fact that animal experiments... have with few exceptions shown that pure coal dust produces no fibrogenic reaction." Fibrosis is the formation of scar tissue and a clear sign of damage to the lung. In fact, the experimental evidence exonerated pure coal dust and pointed to silica as the cause of respiratory disease.[3]

However, the animal data were contradicted by the discovery that men who worked with pure coal dust or carbon alone, also developed pneumoconiosis.[1,2] Such evidence shows that coal dust can cause lung disease even in the absence of silica. The experimental results were further undermined when coal dust, collected at a coal face where pneumoconiosis among miners was high, proved innocuous to laboratory rats![2]

References

1) W.K.C.Morgan in *Occupational Lung Diseases*, Eds. W.K.C.Morgan & A.Seaton (Saunders, 1982).
2) *British Medical Journal*, 1953, January 17, 144-146.
3) L.U.Gardner, *Journal of the American Medical Association*, 1938, November 19, 1925-1936; *Chronic Pulmonary Disease in South Wales III Experimental Studies*, Medical Research Council Special Report Series No.250 (HMSO, 1945).

ANIMAL SKIN TESTS NOT UP TO SCRATCH

Many people suffer dermatitis when they come into contact with nickel compounds as they are considered potent skin sensitizers.[1] Nickel is recognised as the single most common cause of contact dermatitis in women and many of those who suffer prolonged eczema receive disability pensions.[2] In people exposed occupationally, the condition is known as "Nickel itch".

In contrast, nickel is not a potent skin sensitizer in most of the animal tests used to predict allergic responses.[3] The Draize guinea pig test, for instance, suggests that nickel does not cause allergic reactions. Even in the two most widely used animal procedures, nickel produces either no response (the Buehler Test) or only a moderate response (the Maximization Test). Both methods also use guinea pigs.

References
1) *Medical Toxicology*, Eds. M.J.Ellenhorn & D.G.Barceloux (Elsevier, 1988).
2) *Textbook of Dermatology Vol.1,* 5th edition, Eds. R.H.Champion et al (Blackwell Scientific Publications, 1992).
3) P.A.Botham et al, *Food & Chemical Toxicology*, 1991, vol.29, 275-286.

MONKEY EXPERIMENTS PUT MALARIA PATIENTS AT RISK

The use of monkeys to investigate malaria led to the suggestion that coma in human patients is due to an increased amount of protein in the cerebro-spinal fluid, and that this leakage could be corrected with steroids.[1] But in people, steroids do not help with coma. On the contrary, they actually prove harmful.[2] Among survivors, for instance, coma is *prolonged* by 16 hours, while complications such as pneumonia, urinary tract infections, convulsions and gastrointestinal tract bleeding, developed more frequently in patients receiving steroids. Subsequent clinical observations of malaria victims have shown that "the monkey model may simply not be relevant."[1]

References

1) *Lancet*, 1987, May 2, 1016.
2) D.A.Warrell et al, *New England Journal of Medicine*, 1982, February 11, 313-319.

BLOOD CELL DAMAGE MISSED BY ANIMAL TESTING

The antidepressant drug mianserin can cause potentially fatal blood disorders and the *British National Formulary* recommends that patients should have full blood counts every 4 weeks during the first 3 months of treatment.[1] By early 1988 the World Health Organisation Collaborative Centre for International Drug Monitoring had collected 321 reports referring to white blood cell disorders. The effects had not been predicted by animal tests,[2] but subsequent studies showed that they could be observed in test tube experiments with human tissues.[3]

References
1) *British National Formulary*, No.26 (BMA & the Royal Pharmaceutical Society of GB, 1993).
2) H.M.Clink, *British Journal of Clinical Pharmacology*, 1983, vol.15, 291S-293S.
3) P.Roberts et al, *Drug Metabolism & Disposition*, 1991, vol.19, 841-843.

DOG RESEARCH UNDERMINES HEART VALVE DEVELOPMENT

Dogs are favourite animals in cardiac research and many experiments were carried out to develop an artificial mitral valve. However, the artificial valves almost always produced fatal blood clots in these animals,[1] with the result that many surgeons were deterred from carrying out human trials.[2]

Like other experimental surgeons, Starr and Edwards encountered the familiar problem of blood clots but eventually decided on a "caged-ball" device.[3] Other designs were uniformly fatal to the animals and whilst 6 of the 7 dogs receiving the caged ball valve died within 17 days, one did survive for some months. Fortunately, the new valve proved far more successful in clinical trials where blood clotting was not a problem.[4] The surgeons concluded that "the marked propensity of the dog to thrombotic occlusion [blood clotting] or massive embolization from a mitral prosthesis is not shared by the human being."[5]

Starr and Edwards wanted to carry out further animal testing of their new caged ball device but could not use the valve that proved so successful in patients because it nearly always killed the dogs. Instead, they designed a *different* valve specifically for use in these animals! The modified valve did not kill the animals so frequently: even so, 78% still died within 46 days. It was noted that "species differences have therefore led to the use in this clinic of an unshielded ball valve for human mitral replacement and a shielded ball valve as the prosthesis of choice for further testing in the dog."[5]

The successful *clinical* application of another early design of mitral valve replacement cast further doubt on the value of animal research, since none of the dogs used in preclinical tests survived beyond 40 hours![6]

References

1) A.V.Doumanian & F.H.Ellis, *Journal of Thoracic & Cardiovascular Surgery*, 1961, vol.42, 683-695.
2) G.H.A.Clowes Jr. *Annals of Surgery*, 1961, vol.154, 740.
3) A.Starr, *American College of Surgeons, Surgical Forum*, 1960, vol.11, 258-260.
4) A.Starr & M.L.Edwards, *Annals of Surgery*, 1961, vol.154, 726-740.
5) A.Starr & M.L.Edwards, *Journal of Thoracic & Cardiovascular Surgery*, 1961, vol.42, 673-682.
6) N.S.Braunwald et al, *Journal of Thoracic & Cardiovascular Surgery*, 1960, vol.40, 1-11.

ANIMAL TESTS USED TO PROMOTE 'SUPERIOR' ARTHRITIS DRUG

A major hazard of the anti-inflammatory drugs used to treat arthritis is that they damage the stomach.[1] So serious is the problem that any drug free of this side-effect would have an enormous advantage over its competitors.

The anti-inflammatory drug Surgam appeared to have these advantages because it was promoted by the company, Roussel Laboratories, as giving "gastric protection". However, the claims were made on the basis of animal tests and could not be confirmed in clinical trials. As a result of their promotional claims, Roussel were found guilty of misleading advertising and fined £20,000. A report of the case in the *Lancet* described how expert witnesses for *both* sides, "...agreed that animal data could not safely be extrapolated to man."[2]

References
1) R.Cockel, *Gut*, 1987, vol.28, 515-518.
2) J.Collier & A.Herxheimer, *Lancet*, 1987, January 10, 113-114.

FATAL DIURETIC SEEMED SAFE

The diuretic drug Selacryn was introduced in 1979 but withdrawn from the US market only a year later after 363 reports of liver damage including 24 fatalities.[1] In many other countries, including the UK, development of the drug was cancelled.[2] Selacryn's harmful effects were unexpected since they had not been detected in animal experiments.[1]

References
1) S.Takagi et al, *Toxicology Letters*, 1991, vol.55, 287-293.
2) C.Spriet-Pourra & M.Auriche, *Drug Withdrawal from Sale* (PJB Publications, 1988).

ANGINA DRUG'S FATAL EFFECTS

Perhexiline was first marketed in France during the 1970s as a treatment for angina. But concern over its side-effects, especially fatal cases of liver damage, led to withdrawal in the UK, while in some countries it was never licensed at all. Indeed, some argue that "its use should be completely avoided." [1]

The dangers were not predicted by animal tests [2] and administration of high doses to several species for up to 2 years produced no effect on the liver.[3] According to Richardson Merrell, the company marketing perhexiline, "...there has been an inordinate amount of animal work done..At this point we simply have been unable to induce hepatic [liver] disease in any species." [4]

Perhexiline's harmful effects arise in individuals whose body chemistry has been altered by genetic factors, making them more sensitive to the drug. Reliance on animal tests can therefore be seriously misleading since they provide no basis for such subtle predictions.

References
1) D.G.McDevitt & A.M.MacConnachie in *Meyler's Side Effects of Drugs,* 11th edition,Ed. M.N.G.Dukes (Elsevier,1988).
2) C.T.Eason et al, *Regulatory Toxicology & Pharmacology,* 1990, vol.11, 288-307.
3) J.W.Newberne, *Postgraduate Medical Journal,* 1973, vol.49, April Suppl., 125-129.
4) ibid, p.130.

MENTHOL & EYE IRRITATION

Menthol is an ingredient of many cough and cold remedies and is used as an inhalent to relieve symptoms of bronchitis, sinusitis and similar conditions. It can also be used as an ointment for application to the chest or nostrils. If menthol accidentally comes into contact with the eye, it produces a temporary burning sensation lasting 15-30 minutes, but there are no after effects. In contrast, menthol causes "severe damage" to the rabbit's eye.[1]

Reference

1) W.M.Grant, *Toxicology of the Eye*, 2nd edition (Charles Thomas,1974).

"NON-TOXIC" OINTMENT PROVES DANGEROUS

The success of selenium disulphide (Selsun) as an antidandruff shampoo, led to the suggestion that it might also be useful for the treatment of blepharitis, a similar but painful condition involving the eyelids. Trials were carried out in which an ointment containing 0.5% selenium disulphide was applied to the lid margins. However, the ointment proved irritating if it accidentally came into contact with the conjunctiva and one patient developed "moderately severe conjunctivitis."[1] In contrast, animal experiments have shown that "Selenium disulphide 0.5% ophthalmic ointment is *nontoxic* to rabbit corneas or conjunctivas" (emphasis added).[2]

References

1) G.C.Bahn, *Southern Medical Journal*, 1954, vol.47, 749-752.
2) J.W.Rosenthal & H.Adler, *Southern Medical Journal*, 1962, March, 318.

SAFE CLEANING AGENTS DAMAGE ANIMAL VICTIMS

Researchers have discovered that coconut soap causes skin irritation in rabbits. During a comparison of human and animal test data for a selection of household and industrial products, Proctor and Gamble scientists found that while coconut soap had a "negligible" effect on the skin of volunteers, it produced "moderate" irritation in rabbits.[1] Pine oil cleaner also produced "moderate" irritation in rabbits (and guinea pigs) but only a slight effect on human skin.

Other substances which produced insignificant effects on human skin but irritation in animals included high and low carbonate detergents, phosphate detergents, enzyme detergent, sodium carbonate and even lemon juice! Overall, only 6 of 24 products tested had the same effects in people, rabbits and guinea pigs. The report concluded that "Neither the rabbit nor the guinea pig provides an accurate model for human skin. The skin responses of these animals differ in both degree and in kind from those found in human skin."[1]

Similar conclusions have been reached for cosmetic ingredients. Scientists at the Warner Lambert Research Institute in New Jersey note that "...animal skin is entirely different from human skin and that there may be no correlation between the mildness of a raw material on a rabbit's back and its safety during use on a human face." They describe how the cosmetic ingredient isopropyl myristate is considered safe for use on the human body but causes irritation to rabbits. [2]

References

1) G.A.Nixon et al, *Toxicology & Applied Pharmacology*, 1975, vol.31, 481-490.
2) M.M. Rieger & G.W.Battista, *Journal of the Society of Cosmetic Chemists*, 1964, vol.15, 161-172.

MORPHINE MANIA

Morphine remains the most valuable analgesic for severe pain [1] yet has such a peculiar effect in some species that had it been tested on, say cats, prior to human studies, it could have been rejected. In these animals the drug produces a condition known as "morphine mania" which leaves them highly excitable and apprehensive. Their movements are irregular and jerky, and their pupils are abnormally dilated.[2] While morphine produces hyperexcitement in cats, it has the opposite, calming effect in people.[3] Furthermore, their pupils may be *contracted*.[1] Fortunately the drug was discovered through human studies and only later tested on animals. [4]

References

1) *British National Formulary*, no.26 (BMA & the Royal Pharmaceutical Society of G.B.,1993).
2) F.M.Sturtevant & V.A.Drill, *Nature*, 1957, June 15, 1253.
3) B.Brodie, *Clinical Pharmacology & Therapeutics*, 1962, vol.3, 374-380.
4) J.T.Litchfield in *Drugs in our Society*, Ed. P.Talalay (Johns Hopkins, 1964).

CHEMOTHERAPY AID WITHDRAWN

Domperidone is used for the treatment of nausea and vomitting, particularly that caused by anticancer drug therapy. In 1986 the injectable form of the drug was withdrawn worldwide [1] because of potentially hazardous heart rhythm disturbances. The dangers had not been predicted by animal experiments [2] and in dogs, the animal traditionally used to assess effects on the heart, more than 70 times the recommended human dose produced no changes in the electrocardiogram.[3]

References

1) C.Spriet-Pourra & M.Auriche, *Drug Withdrawal from Sale*,(PJB Publications,1988).
2) R.Heywood in *Animal Toxicity Studies: Their Relevance for Man*, Eds. C.E.Lumley & S.R.Walker (Quay Publications, 1990).
3) R.N.Brogden et al, *Drugs*, 1982, vol.24, 360-400.

NATURAL SKIN SUBSTANCE HARMS ANIMALS

Squalene is a natural constituent of human sebum, the substance formed by sebaceous glands around the roots of hairs to keep the skin lubricated and supple. Although a natural human product, squalene has still been applied to the skin of rabbits and guinea pigs, where it actually produced hair *loss*. This is obviously not the case in people,[1] and it has been extensively and safely employed in cosmetics.[2]

References
1) B.Boughton et al, *Journal of Investigative Dermatology*, 1955, vol.24, 179-189.
2) M.M.Rieger & G.W.Battista, *Journal of the Society of Cosmetic Chemists*, 1964, vol.15, 161-172.

HEART TREATMENT WITHDRAWN

Prenylamine, a treatment for angina, was withdrawn from the UK market in 1988,[1] the main problem being that the drug caused ventricular tachycardia, a condition in which the heart beats abnormally fast. The side-effect caused patients to faint. In contrast, animal experiments carried out at the University of Eoteborg in Sweden revealed that in cats, rabbits and guinea pigs, prenylamine *reduced* the heart rate by up to 25%.[2] In cats, for instance, a dose of prenylamine reduced heart rate from 225 beats per minute to 171.

References
1) C.Spriet-Pourra & M.Auriche, *Drug Withdrawal from Sale* (PJB Publications, 1988).
2) H.Obianwu, *Acta Pharmacology et Toxicology*, 1967, vol.25, 127-140.

DOCTORS WARN AGAINST "SAFE" EYE TREATMENT

In 1951, physicians at the University of California Medical School in San Francisco, warned ophthalmologists against the prolonged use of furmethide in the treatment of glaucoma.[1] They noted that permanent obstruction of the tear passages occured in over 70% of patients where the drug was used for more than 3 months.

Eleven years earlier, researchers had reported experiments on animals' eyes, pronouncing the drug "entirely safe" and worthy of clinical trial.[2] The tests were performed on rats, guinea pigs and rabbits and continued for several months.

References

1) R.N.Shaffer & W.L.Ridgway, *American Journal of Ophthalmology*, 1951, vol.34, 718-720.
2) A.Myerson & W.Thau, *Archives of Ophthalmology*, 1940, vol.24, 758-760.

ANIMAL-TESTED ARTHRITIS DRUGS KILLED THOUSANDS

Phenylbutazone (Butazolidine) was once widely employed for the treatment of arthritis but reports of aplastic anaemia, an often fatal blood disease caused by damage to the bone marrow, led to the drug's withdrawal in some countries and to its restriction in others, notably America, France and the UK.[1]

On the basis of animal tests, phenylbutazone had seemed a safe drug with no toxic effects observed in rats even after administration of 5-10 times the dose used for people.[2] In particular, phenylbutazone's harmful effect on the bone marrow had not been predicted,[3] and one year after marketing, researchers noted that "there have been no published reports of serious effects...on the hemopoietic [blood forming] system...in the experimental animal."[4] Later research showed that the dangers could be identified by test-tube experiments with human bone marrow cells.[5]

It has been estimated that phenylbutazone and oxyphenbutazone, a closely related drug that also causes aplastic anaemia, have been reponsible for 10,000 deaths worldwide.[6] Oxyphenbutazone (Tanderil) was withdrawn altogether in 1985.

References
1) C.Spriet-Pourra & M.Auriche, *Drug Withdrawal from Sale* (PJB Publications, 1988).
2) C.Hinz & L.M.Gaines, *Journal of the American Medical Association*, 1953, vol.151, 38-39.
3) R.Heywood in *Animal Toxicity Studies: Their Relevance for Man*, Eds. C.E.Lumley & S.R.Walker (Quay Publishing, 1990).
4) O.Steinbrocker et al, *Journal of the American Medical Association*, 1952, November 15, 1087-1091.
5) C.S.Smith et al, *Biochemical Pharmacology*, 1977, vol.26, 847-852.
6) Estimate by Dr Sidney Wolfe in *Lancet*, 1984, February 11, 353.

THE CHLOROFORM CONTROVERSY

The anaesthetics ether, nitrous oxide and chloroform originated from experiments carried out by physicians and scientists on themselves, and, together with the introduction of hygienic conditions, enabled surgery to emerge from the dark ages.[1] Because of their high safety profile, nitrous oxide and ether have stood the test of time. In the case of chloroform, entrenched attitudes and contradictory animal experiments allowed a toxic drug to outlive its value and remain in use for over 100 years. [2]

Deaths from chloroform were reported almost weekly during the second half of the 19th century and between 1887 and 1896 there were 376 fatalities in England and Wales. Many believed the deaths resulted from respiratory failure but that risks could be minimised by appropriate administration of the drug and by devoting attention to the patient's breathing in order to detect early warning signs. The alternative (correct) explanation, that chloroform has a direct effect on the heart, was discounted.

Unfortunately, animal experiments carried out by the Hyderabad Commissions of 1888 and 1889 supported the view that chloroform affects the respiration rather than the heart.[2] In a famous telegram to the *Lancet*,[3] Lauder Brunton summarised results from the Second Commission: " Four hundred and ninety dogs, horses, goats, cats and rabbits used...Results most instructive. Danger from chloroform is asphyxia or overdose: none whatever heart direct." Anaesthetists must have been reassured to hear Brunton's conclusion that chloroform "never causes sudden death from stoppage of the heart."

In 1893, clinical observations completely contradicted the conclusions from Hyderabad and showed that heart failure is the commonest cause of death from chloroform.[2] Nevertheless, use of the drug continued until the 1950s and the Hyderabad Commissions were later blamed for failing to recognise species differences.[2]

References
1) R.Sharpe, *The Cruel Deception: the use of animals in medical research* (Thorsons, 1988).
2) K.B.Thomas, *Proceedings of the Royal Society of Medicine*, 1974, vol.67, 723-730.
3) *Lancet*, 1889, December 7, 1183.

ANAEMIA CURE FAILS IN ANIMALS

When treating iron-deficiency anaemia, doctors prefer their patients to take iron by mouth, but should oral therapy fail, the iron is administered by injection.[1] Injectable iron remedies were introduced during the 1930s but could easily have been discarded. At that time, experiments in which anaemias were artificially induced in animals by iron deficiency or by repeated haemorrhage, led to the conclusion that injecting iron had *no* therapeutic value.[2] Fortunately, clinical studies proved that anaemic patients could be cured in this way.

Iron sorbitol is one form of injectable iron that might have been rejected for a different reason. Administration to rats and rabbits caused cancer at the injection site and the implications for human therapeutics appeared serious. However, clinical experience has revealed no real hazard to patients.[3]

References

1) *British National Formulary*, No.26 (BMA & Royal Pharmaceutical Society of G.B., 1993).
2) G.N.Burger & L.J.Witts, *Proceedings of the Royal Society of Medicine*, 1934, vol.27, 447-455.
3) M.Weatherall, *Nature*, 1982, April 1, 387-390.

RESEARCH 'PARALYZED' BY ANIMAL MODELS

During the twentieth century, extensive research has been carried out to develop an animal model that mimics spinal cord injuries (SCI) in people.[1] A common procedure is to drop weights onto the spinal cord of cats.[2] By using animals, researchers hoped to devise promising therapies and discover new insights into the condition.However,virtually no treatments have been developed that work in human patients.[1] In 1988 for instance, Dennis Maiman of the Department of Neurosurgery at the Medical College of Wisconsin,Milwaukee, noted that "In the last two decades at least 22 agents have been found to be therapeutic in experimental SCI... Unfortunately, to date none of these has been proven effective in clinical SCI."[1] The failure to accurately predict human responses is attributed to the artifical nature of the animal model.

In 1990, however, clinical trials did show that high doses of steroids could be beneficial. Some have credited animal tests with the discovery but the claim has been challenged. It is argued that the animal experiments were not only unnecessary but they gave inconsistent results, with some tests suggesting the therapy would actually *fail*![2]

References
1) D.Maiman, *Journal of the American Paraplegia Society*, 1988, vol.11, 23-25.
2) S.R.Kaufman, *Perspectives on Medical Research*, 1990, vol.2, 1-12.

ANTI-CANCER HOPE ABANDONED

When animal researchers tested a newly discovered substance, psicofuranine, for anti-cancer activity, they found contradictory evidence in rats and mice.[1] The drug proved active against several tumours in laboratory rats but had no effect on 3 different cancers in mice. Unfortunately doctors could not properly assess the drug against human cancer since psicofuranine produced severe and unexpected side-effects in early human trials, thus terminating any further investigation in people. The drug damaged the heart yet no cardiac toxicity had been found in mice, rats, dogs or monkeys. [1]

Although clinical study of psicofuranine was abandoned, further animal experiments were carried out in an attempt to reproduce the heart problems seen in people. Once again, no cardiac toxicity could be observed even when dogs and monkeys were given 5-10 times the harmful human dose.[1]

Reference

1) C.G.Smith et al, *Journal of International Medical Research*, 1973, vol.1, 489-503.

UNEXPECTED EYE PROBLEMS LED TO DRUG REJECTION

During clinical trials, the anticancer drug sparsomycin produced eye damage, resulting in serious blind spots in 3 of the 5 patients. Although sparsomycin was highly toxic to several animal species, as would be expected for an anticancer drug, no specific effect on the eye had been found.[1] After the eye problems had been reported, further attempts were made to induce the condition in rats and monkeys but these also failed even though rats were dosed every day for 2 weeks with 30-300 times the amount found to harm people.[1] No retinal toxicity was observed in additional animal tests and further experimentation was adandoned, as was the drug.

Reference

1) C.G.Smith et al, *Journal of International Medical Research*, 1973, vol.1, 489-503.

CORTICOSTEROIDS & BIRTH DEFECTS

Contrary to human experience,experiments on pregnant mice and rabbits would suggest that corticosteroids are very dangerous to the unborn child. In some strains of mice cortisone produces cleft palate in up to 100% of the offspring.[1] With rabbits, corticosteroids mainly affect the heart but can also cause severe growth retardation in the uterus and death of the foetus. However, scientists have found "very wide species variation"[2] and cortisone is not considered harmful to human babies.[1] Rats and monkeys are also "very tolerant of corticosteroids in pregnancy, abnormalities or growth retardation only occurring uncommonly, with high doses of the most potent compounds."[2]

References
1) R.M.Ward & T.P.Green, *Pharmacology & Therapeutics*, 1988, vol.36, 326.
2) R.K.Sidhu in *Drugs & Pregnancy: Human Teratogenesis & Related Problems*, Ed. D.F.Hawkins (Churchill Livingstone, 1983).

"HARMLESS" ANTIDEPRESSANT DAMAGED LIVER

Iproniazid was originally developed as a treatment for tuberculosis but found use as an antidepressant. Although considered "harmless" on the basis of animal tests,[1] iproniazid produced fatal cases of liver damage in human patients and the drug was eventually abandoned.[2]

References

1) J.Boyer in *Clinical Pharmacology, Basic Principles in Therapeutics,* 2nd edition, Eds. K.L.Melmon & H.F.Morrelli (MacMillan, 1978).
2) B.Blackwell & J.S.Simon in *Side Effects of Drugs Annual 13,* Eds. M.N.G.Dukes & L.Beeley (Elsevier, 1989).

THALIDOMIDE

Thalidomide was first introduced as a sedative by the German drug company Chemie Grünenthal in 1957, and by the Distillers company in Britain a year later. Although animals could tolerate massive doses without ill-effect,[1] thalidomide was soon found to cause peripheral neuritis in human patients: feelings of numbness were followed by severe muscular cramps, weakness of the limbs and a lack of co-ordination.

The Australian obstetrician William McBride was first alerted to thalidomide's most notorious side-effect after seeing 3 babies born with very unusual birth defects. Unfortunately, his warnings to the medical profession were delayed because he tried to "confirm" his observations by testing the drug in mice and guinea pigs, both of whom proved resistant to the drug.[2] Only after seeing further human cases did McBride publish his findings.

Although not specifically tested for birth defects prior to marketing, subsequent experiments revealed "extreme variability in species susceptibility to thalidomide."[3] For instance, mice could safely tolerate 8000 times the dose found harmful to human babies.[4] In his book *Drugs as Teratogens*, Schardein writes, "in approximately 10 strains of rats, 15 strains of mice, eleven breeds of rabbit, two breeds of dogs, three strains of hamsters, eight species of primates and in other such varied species as cats, armadillos, guinea pigs, swine and ferrets in which thalidomide has been tested,teratogenic effects [birth defects] have been induced only occasionally." Scientists eventually discovered that birth defects similar to those found in people could be induced in certain types of rabbit and primate. Nevertheless, New Zealand white rabbits had to be dosed with 300 times the amount dangerous to humans.[5]

The thalidomide disaster prompted additional,extensive testing of drugs and chemicals in pregnant animals,but some scientists believe that "animal malformations seldom correlate with those of humans."[6] Furthermore, "..no animal model has been found which responds satisfactorily to all known teratologic agents in humans to permit reliable screening of substances for their teratologic potential. Careful surveillance, reporting and prospective study ...remain the mainstays for detection of adverse effects following foetal drug exposure."[6]

References

1) R.D.Mann, *Modern Drug Use, an Enquiry on Historical Principles* (MTP Press, 1984).
2) The Sunday Times "Insight" Team, *Suffer the Children - The Story of Thalidomide* (Andre Deutsche, 1979).
3) T.H.Shepard, *Catalogue of Teratogenic Agents* (Johns Hopkins Press, 1976).
4) S.K.Keller & M.K.Smith, *Teratogenesis, Carcinogenesis & Mutagenesis,* 1982, vol.2, 361-374.
5) New Zealand White rabbits were sensitive to doses of 150mg/Kg of thalidomide (ref.6) whilst the dangerous human dose was 0.5mg/Kg (ref.4).
6) R.M.Ward & T.P.Green, *Pharmacology & Therapeutics*, 1988, vol.36, 326.

BEAGLE DOGS MISLEAD CANCER RESEARCH

Mitoxantrone was developed in the hope of providing effective cancer treatment without side-effects on the heart. Animal researchers were presumably reassured when tests on beagle dogs "failed to demonstrate cardiac failure."[1] But in clinical trials several patients suffered side-effects including heart failure, and more widespread use of the drug confirmed that cardiac toxicity is a major problem. For instance, data from 3,360 patients receiving mitoxantrone included 88 reports of cardiac side effects with 29 cases of heart failure.[2] And a recent Chinese study suggested that 20% of patients developed cardiotoxicity following treatment with mitoxantrone.[3]

References

1) R.Stuart Harris et al, *Lancet*, 1984, July 28, 219-220.
2) *Martindale: The Extra Pharmacopoeia*, 29th edition, Ed. J.E.F.Reynolds (Pharmceutical Press, 1989).
3) A.Stanley & G.Blackledge in *Side Effects of Drugs,Annual 15*, Eds. M.N.G.Dukes & J.K.Aronson (Elsevier,1991).

'HARMLESS' ULCER DRUG COULD CAUSE HEART FAILURE

Carbenoxalone was introduced during the 1960s for the treatment of peptic ulcers but caused salt and water retention in some patients leading to high blood pressure, swelling, weight gain, muscle weakness and heart failure. Other drugs are now preferred, says the *British National Formulary,* but if carbenoxalone is to be used, patients should be monitored carefully during treatment.[1]

Prior to marketing, animal tests had given the impression that carbenoxalone was safe, having revealed no harmful effects.[2] These tests were carried out on rodents but scientists then realised that people metabolised carbenoxalone quite differently to rats, mice and rabbits. Further experiments were therefore undertaken with dogs and monkeys but again, there was no evidence of toxicity. [2]

References
1) *British National Formulary*, no.26 (BMA & the Royal Pharmaceutical Society of G.B., 1993).
2) C.T.Eason et al, *Regulatory Toxicology & Pharmacology*, 1990, vol.11, 288-307.

ANTIBIOTIC'S DEADLY SIDE-EFFECT

Britain's Committee on Safety of Medicines has alerted doctors to the dangers of clindamycin, an antibiotic whose most serious side-effect is an intestinal disease called pseudomembraneous colitis. The condition leads to diarrhoea and sometimes proves fatal. By 1980, 12 years after the drug was marketed in the UK, 36 deaths had been reported.[1] Although the problem can occur with other antibiotics, it is most frequently seen with clindamycin, and the *British National Formulary* warns that patients should stop taking the drug immediately if diarrhoea develops.

In contrast, rats and dogs given clindamycin every day for a year, could tolerate *12 times* the maximum recommended human dose.[2]

References

1) G.R.Venning, *British Medical Journal*, 1983, January 15, 199-202.
2) *The British National Formulary* (No.26,1993) lists the maximum oral dose for severe infections as 450mg every 6 hours i.e. 25mg/kg for a person weighing 70 kg taking 4 doses in 24 hours. Rats and dogs could tolerate more than 300mg/kg (J.E.Gray et al,*Toxicology & Applied Pharmacology*, 1972, vol.21, 516-531.)

LEUKEMIC MICE FAIL CANCER PATIENTS

For decades, America's National Cancer Institute (NCI) has used animals in the search for new drugs. Tens of thousands of chemicals have been assessed in mice given leukemia but the method has proved highly inefficient. One scientist estimates that for every 30-40 drugs effective in treating mice with cancer, only one will work in people,[1] which suggests that during clinical trials many cancer patients will be exposed to the severe toxicity of anticancer drugs without any corresponding benefit. During the 1980s, researchers acknowledged that the NCI's traditional approach was failing to identify promising new treatments against any of the main cancers.[2,3]

In the new strategy, mice have been replaced by test-tube studies with human cancer cells, at least for preliminary experiments. Drugs showing promising activity are then subject to further animal tests so there is still the risk of misleading predictions.[4] As an alternative, drugs could be further assessed using fresh human tumour tissue from biopsies or therapeutic operations.[5] Results would then be directly relevant to people.[4]

References
1) D.D.Von Hoff, *Journal of the American Medical Association*, 1979, August 10, 503.
2) R.Kolberg, *Journal of NIH Research*, 1990, vol.2, 82-84.
3) A.Pihl, *International Journal of Cancer*, 1986, vol.37, 1-5.
4) S.E.Salmon, *Cloning of Human Tumor Stem Cells* (Alan Liss, 1980).
5) C.W.Taylor et al, *Journal of the National Cancer Institute*, 1992, vol.84, 489-494.

THE FIRST BETA-BLOCKERS

Beta-blockers were developed for the treatment of heart conditions and the first agents to be administered to human patients were pronethalol and propranolol. Ironically, pronethalol proved generally safe and effective in laboratory animals but failed the clinical test, while propranolol appeared toxic in many animal experiments yet is widely used in clinical practice.

Pronethalol was "well tolerated" by rats and dogs in prolonged toxicity tests at high doses, except for occasional effects on the central nervous system.[1] However, clinical trials revealed an unacceptable number of side-effects [2] including heart failure, a hazard not predicted by animal experiments.[1] Shortly after, long term tests in a certain (Alderley Park) strain of laboratory mouse produced cancer of the thymous gland but no carcinogenic effects were ever found in rats, guinea pigs, dogs, monkeys or other types of mouse.[1]

Pronethalol was quickly replaced by propranolol but tests in rats, dogs and mice put further development in jeopardy.[3] Moderate to high doses caused rats to collapse and dogs to vomit severely.[1] Deaths were also seen in mice shortly after dosing. When the amount of drug was reduced to that used clinically, propranolol was said to be "well tolerated". Even so, some of the rats still had heart lesions.[1]

Later clinical observations showed that propranolol could also lower the blood pressure,[4] and today beta-blockers are widely used for the treatment of high blood pressure.

References

1) J.M.Cruickshank et al in *Safety Testing of New Drugs*,Eds. D.R.Laurence et al (Academic Press,1984)
2) W.Sneader, *Drug Discovery: the evolution of modern medicine* (Wiley, 1985)
3) D.R.Laurence et al (Eds.), *Safety Testing of New Drugs* (Academic Press,1984)
4) E.S.Snell, *Pharmacy International*, 1986, February, 33-37.

MINOR TRANQUILLIZERS PRODUCE MAJOR PROBLEMS

Librium and Valium were the first of a new type of tranquillizing drug to be introduced during the early 1960s. They were called "minor tranquillizers" (benzodiazepines) and many similar drugs quickly followed. They soon became the most widely used of all prescribed drugs. Almost immediately after the introduction of Librium and Valium, doctors reported cases of dependence but it was generally assumed that high doses were necessary.[1] At the usual therapeutic amounts, dependence was thought to be uncommon and not a serious problem. The idea prevailed for 20 years and received support from laboratory research since "animal experiments...do not indicate the potential for the development in the human of dependence at therapeutic dosage levels."[2]

It is known, however, that "animal studies...do not predict clinical dependence potential reliably,"[3] and more careful human observations revealed that tranquillizers could induce dependence at ordinary doses. By the mid-1980s, an estimated 500,000 people in Britain alone may have been addicted to their treatment.[4]

References
1) H.Petursson & M.Lader, *Dependence on Tranquillizers* (Oxford University Press, 1984).
2) J.Marks, *The Benzodiazepines* (MTP Press, 1978).
3) *Drug & Therapeutics Bulletin*, 1989, vol.27, 28.
4) *The Benzodiazepines in Current Clinical Practice*, Eds. H.Freeman & Y.Rue (Royal Society of Medicine Services, 1987).

RIFAMPICIN & THE PILL

In 1971 doctors reported unexpected pregnancies among women taking the "pill".[1] Of 88 women taking oral contraceptives in addition to the antituberculous drug rifampicin, 75% suffered disturbances to their menstrual cycle, and 5 became pregnant. The rifampicin had stimulated the patient's liver to metabolise, or breakdown, the pill more rapidly. Consequently, far less contraceptive remained to protect the women from pregnancy. The *British National Formulary* (1993) now tells doctors prescribing rifampicin to "advise patients on oral contraceptives to use additional means [of contraception]."

Further reports showed that rifampicin accelerates the breakdown of many other medicines.[2] An example is methadone where rifampicin led to withdrawal symptoms by reducing the amount of drug. Another patient rejected their kidney graft because rifampicin had diminished the dose of immunosuppressive drug cyclosporin.

Rifampicin's peculiar effect had not been predicted by animal experiments.[3] Following discovery of the effects in people, further animal tests were carried out but these proved contradictory. For instance, the drug's action could not be reproduced in rats.[4] In mice, however, *prolonged* treatment with rifampicin did stimulate the liver's metabolic processes but a *single* dose had the opposite effect, slowing down metabolism.[4] Nevertheless, the problems with rifampicin might have been predicted had scientists used human liver tissue for their tests.[5]

References

1) Reported in J.P.Mumford, *British Medical Journal*, 1974, May 11, 333-334.
2) H.Meyer et al in *Meyler's Side Effects of Drugs*, 11th edition, Ed. M.N.G.Dukes (Elsevier, 1988).
3) E.Nieschlag, *Pharmacology & Therapeutics*, 1979, vol.5, 407-409.
4) D.Pessayre & P.Mazel, *Biochemical Pharmacology*, 1976, vol.25, 943-949.
5) A.M.Jezequel et al, *Gut*, 1971, vol.12, 984-987.

BREAST-CANCER DRUG OVERCOMES CONFLICTING DATA

It is a minor miracle that tamoxifen overcame a succession of conflicting animal data to find a place in clinical practice. The drug was developed by ICI during the 1960s as an oral contraceptive and in rats tamoxifen can prevent ovulation or terminate pregnancy.[1] In women however, tamoxifen *stimulates* ovulation and is listed as a treatment for infertility![2]

Tamoxifen is also used in breast cancer therapy where it works by blocking the action of oestrogen in breast tissue. The drug is therefore called an "anti-oestrogen." In monkeys, and rats at low doses, tamoxifen also acts as an anti-oestrogen but in mice, dogs, and rats at high doses, the drug has the opposite effect, behaving like an oestrogen.[1] The use of animals to investigate these effects is bedevilled with problems since "significant species variation has been observed in target tissue response to oestrogens and anti-oestrogens making it hazardous to predict therapeutic activity in the human by extrapolation of effects in experimental animals..."[3]

Animal tests have also given conflicting results in assessing the drug's harmful effects, with tamoxifen producing liver tumours in rats but not mice.[4] Liver cancer does not seem to be a problem for human patients and only two cases have been reported in around 3 million women who have received the drug. Furthermore, tamoxifen is known to be processed differently by rats and people. John Patterson, medical director at ICI, explains that "If this was a new chemical entity those findings in rats would have caused us to stop its development, but the human experience gave us confidence."[5]

Nevertheless the rat data led to a major row between Britain's two biggest cancer charities and the Medical Research Council over trials of tamoxifen for the prevention of breast cancer, in which the drug is given to *healthy* women. Most proponents of the trial considered the rat experiments nothing to worry about[6,7] but the MRC actually withdrew its support and initiated new animal tests. Embarrassed by the split, one of the cancer charities, the Imperial Cancer Research Fund, stated that "We are going to be in a position where the animal rights people are going to be saying to us 'You ignore animal data when you choose to'."[7]

Ironically, fresh doubt was cast on tamoxifen's preventive role by a subsequent clinical study suggesting an increased risk of womb cancer amongst breast cancer patents being treated with the drug. Whilst questioning whether it should be given to healthy women, the report stressed that for the treatment of breast cancer, the benefits far outweighed the risks.[8]

Overall, tamoxifen has comparatively few serious side effects and according to ICI, the main reason patients stop taking the drug is nausea and vomitting.[1] This must have surprised the company because "None of the toxicological studies produced any evidence of vomitting even though high doses were used in dogs which we consider to be a predictive species for vomitting in man."[1]

References

1) M.J.Tucker et al in *Safety Testing of New Drugs,* Eds. D.R.Laurence et al (Academic Press, 1984)
2) *British National Formulary*, No.26 (BMA & the Royal Pharmaceutical Society of GB, 1993)
3) P.K.Devi in *Pharmacology of Estrogens*, Ed. R.R.Chaudhury (Pergamon Press, 1981)
4) I.N.H. White et al, *Biochemical Pharmacology*, 1993, vol.45, 21-30
5) Reported in P.Brown, *New Scientist*, 1992, February 29, 11.
6) Editorial, *New Scientist*, 1992, March 21, 9.
7) P.Brown, *New Scientist*, 1992, March 21, 12.
8) F.E.van Leeuwen et al, *Lancet*, 1994, February 19, 448-452.

STEROIDS & THE IMMUNE SYSTEM

Because of their potent effects on the immune system, corticosteroid drugs are widely used in medicine. They also have many side-effects which limit their usefulness, and much research has been carried out to discover exactly how the drugs work. However, there are said to be "remarkable differences in susceptibility to glucocorticosteroids between various species," with animals being classified as steroid-resistant or steroid-sensitive.[1] In mice, a steroid-sensitive species, a single dose of cortisone produces a 90% decrease in the thymus, an organ that plays a crucial role in immunity. By contrast, the same dose of cortisone given every day for a week, produced only a 37% decrease in the steroid-resistant guinea pig's thymus. And while steroids inhibit the production of circulating antibodies in sensitive animals, the same effect is difficult to achieve in resistant species.[1]

Most of the research on corticosteroids has been carried out on steroid sensitive species such as rats, mice, rabbits and hamsters whereas *human beings are steroid resistant*.[1] As researchers at the University of Dundee point out "The mode of action of these drugs is very complicated, so it is regrettable that most of the extensive literature on animal experimental work is irrelevant to human therapeutics since many species respond in a very different manner from man."[2] Consequently they concentrated on human clinical studies and test-tube experiments.

References
1) H.N.Claman, *New England Journal of Medicine*, 1972, August 24, 388-397.
2) J.S.Beck & M.C.K.Browning, *Journal of the Royal Society of Medicine*, 1983, vol. 76, 473-479.

X-RAYS & CANCER

In 1956 British doctors drew attention to a link between X-rays during pregnancy and subsequent childhood cancers.[1] Within a few years similar findings were reported in American children. But for a quarter of a century, scientists questioned whether X-rays were actually the cause and cited animal experiments to show that the foetus is not especially sensitive to radiation.[2] However, it seems that compared with other species, the human foetus is more susceptible to the carcinogenic effects of X-rays,[2] and during the 1980s further observational studies confirmed the hazards, particularly in early pregnancy.[3]

References

1) A.M. Stewart et al,*Lancet*, 1956, September 1, 447; *British Medical Journal*, 1958, June 28, 1495-1508.
2) E.B.Harvey et al, *New England Journal of Medicine*, 1985, February 28, 541-545.
3) E.G.Knox et al, *Journal of the Society of Radiological Protection*, 1987, vol.7, 3-15; E.A.Gilman et al, *Journal of Radiological Protection*, 1988, vol.8, 3-8.

THE METHANOL SCANDAL

Methanol is employed in a wide variety of consumer products including solid fuels, antifreeze, windshield wiper fluid, paint remover, varnishes and as a solvent in photocopying machines. It is also imbibed as a cheap alternative to alcohol.

Although methanol is a highly poisonous, potentially lethal substance, this was not realised for many years.[1] Common laboratory species such as rats and mice are resistant to its effects,[2] and experiments during the early years of the 20th century gave the impression that methanol was only slightly toxic, and far less poisonous than alcohol.[3] In fact, methanol is *ten times more toxic* and a single bout of drinking methanol can lead to temporary or permanent blindness in people.[4] This does not happen in rats, mice, dogs, cats, rabbits or chickens.[3] Eventually,in the 1950s, and again during the 1970s, scientists found that the horrifying symptoms of methanol poisoning could be induced in monkeys.[2]

Animal experiments also proved misleading in devising treatment. During the 1920s, good results were achieved using bicarbonate in cases of human poisoning, but tragically the results were undermined by animal experiments. In 1955 an analysis of the subject stated that "it is indeed deplorable that about 30 years elapsed before the good effects of this treatment became commonly known, and unfortunately some still doubt its value. It seems that the authors of medical textbooks have paid more attention to the results of animal experiments than to clinical observations."[3] The treatment not only failed in animals but generally proved fatal, prompting some researchers to advise against it.

Another approach is to administer alcohol in order to reduce the toxicity of methanol. While this is effective in people, animal tests suggested that it would actually *increase* the danger of methanol.

As a result, some discouraged its use in cases of human poisoning.[3] However, both bicarbonate and alcohol have withstood the clinical test and are still recommended for the treatment of methanol poisoning.[1]

References

1) M.J. Ellenhorn & D.G.Barceloux, *Medical Toxicology: Diagnosis & Treatment of Human Poisoning* (Elsevier, 1988).
2) T.R.Tephly, *Life Sciences*, 1991, vol. 48, 1031-1041.
3) O.Roe, *Pharmacological Reviews*, 1955, vol.7, 399-412.
4) P.Wingate, *Medical Encyclopedia* (Penguin, 1983).

OBESITY DRUG'S HORRIFIC SIDE EFFECTS

During the 1960s Swiss doctors noticed a sudden and unexpected rise in a dangerous lung disease called obstructive pulmonary hypertension. The cause was traced to aminorex which had been used since 1965 for the treatment of obesity.[1] The drug produces an increase in lung pressure leading to chest pains, difficulty breathing, fainting spells, heart problems and, in some cases, death.[2] Aminorex's deadly side effect had not been predicted by animal experiments [3] and in 1968 the drug was withdrawn from sale.

Animal experiments continued even after withdrawal but long term administration to rats still failed to induce the disease.[2] In dogs, aminorex did increase lung pressure [1] but its relevance to the human condition is unclear since a later analysis concluded that "pulmonary hypertension cannot be induced in experimental animals even with aminorex..."[4]

References

1) F.Follath et al, *British Medical Journal*, 1971, January 30, 265-266.
2) E.H.Ellinwood & W.J.K.Rockwell in *Meyler's Side Effects of Drugs*, 11th edition, Ed. M.N.G.Dukes (Elsevier,1988)
3) A.D.Dayan in *Risk-Benefit Analysis in Drug Research*, Ed. J.F.Cavalla (MTP Press, 1981).
4) P.H.Connell in *Side Effects of Drugs Annual - 3*, Ed. M.N.G.Dukes (Excerpta Medica, 1979).

DAUGHTERS OF DES

On the basis of animal experiments, the synthetic oestrogen diethylstilbestrol (DES) was suggested as a means of preventing miscarriage.[1] Although no proper human (clinical) trials were carried out,[2] the procedure nevertheless became widely accepted, and between 1948 and 1971, DES was given to some 2-3 million pregnant women in the US alone.

However, DES was ineffective. In 1953, properly controlled clinical trials showed that DES did not work.[3] Tragically, the study failed to report that DES increased abortions, neonatal deaths and premature births, a conclusion that could have been made from the data available in the trial.[4] DES was not only ineffective, it was also unsafe. Just how unsafe was only revealed in 1971 when researchers traced a link between exposure to DES and a previously rare form of vaginal and cervical cancer in daughters of women who had taken the drug during pregnancy.[5] Almost 600 cases have been reported [6] but DES has proved a biological timebomb as side-effects continue to surface in sons and daughters of women who took the drug.

It has been suggested that animal tests provided an early warning of the problems. It is true that in 1938 DES was found to cause *breast* cancer in male mice, but since the cancer-causing potential of other oestrogens varied according to the strain of mouse used,[7] the results could hardly be a serious basis for action. Furthermore, the consensus among animal researchers at the time was that oestrogens did not produce cancer,[7] rather they gave male mice mammary glands and thus made them susceptible to the same cancer-causing factors that operated within female animals. In fact, a summary of the animal data in 1941 found "only meagre evidence" that oestrogens cause cancer of the cervix.[7] Not until the 1970s did it become clear that in contrast to the majority of animal experiments, DES was a potent cause of cervical cancer in women.

References

1) *Health Action International, "Problem Drugs" pack*, 1986, May 13
2) D.Brahams, *Lancet*, 1988, October 15, 916.
3) W.J.Dieckmann et al, *American Journal of Obstetrics & Gynaecology*, 1953, vol.66, 1062-1081.
4) Y.Brackbill & H.W.Berendes, *Lancet*, 1978, September 2, 520.
5) A.L.Herbst et al, *New England Journal of Medicine*, 1971, April 22, 878-881.
6) C.Vanchieri, *Journal of the National Cancer Institute*, 1992, vol.84, 565-566.
7) S.Peller, *Cancer in Man* (McMillan, 1952).

HEART-DRUG FEARS GROUNDLESS

The vital heart drugs digoxin and digitoxin are the pure substances extracted from digitalis whose value in treating heart failure and cardiac arrhythmias originated from studies of human patients.[1,2] However, doctors must be careful not to give too high a dose as they can then be toxic. Fortunately the drugs did not derive from animal experiments since doses considered safe for rats, guinea pigs, dogs, and cats can actually *kill* human patients.[3] Today we know that digoxin's lethal dose is more accurately predicted by test-tube studies with human cells.[4]

Animal tests also suggested that digitalis raised the blood pressure, and as a result, it was once widely taught that the drug would be dangerous for certain patients and should not therefore be given. Thankfully, clinical observations eventually showed this to be incorrect and digitalis can be used with great benefit.[2]

References
1) W.Sneader, *Drug Discovery: The Evolution of Modern Medicine* (Wiley, 1985)
2) T.Lewis, *Clinical Science* (Shaw & Sons Ltd, 1934)
3) G.T.Okita, *Federation Proceedings*, 1967, vol.26, 1125-1130.
4) R.Jover et al, *Toxicology In Vitro*, 1992, vol.6, 47-52.

PETHIDINE ADDICTION

On the basis of experiments with dogs, the narcotic analgesic pethidine was once thought to be non-addictive in people.[1] The side-effect was not anticipated because pethidine is metabolised, or broken down, much more quickly in dogs resulting in less exposure to the drug. In fact, dogs metabolise pethidine more than 6 times faster than people.[2]

Such differences in metabolism are the rule rather than the exception[2,3] and according to Miles Weatherall, former Director of the Wellcome Research Laboratories, "every species has its own metabolic pattern, and no two species are likely to metabolise a drug identically."[4]

References

1) B.Brodie, *Pharmacologist*, 1964, vol.6, 12-26.
2) R.Levine, *Pharmacology: Drug Actions & Reactions* (Little, Brown & Co.,1978)
3) G.Zbinden, *Advances in Pharmacology*, 1963, vol.2, 1-112.
4) M.Weatherall, *Nature*, 1982, April 1, 387-390.

'SAFE' EYE SOLUTIONS FAIL THE HUMAN TEST

Detergents are not only used for domestic and industrial cleaning. In research aimed at increasing penetration of therapeutic drugs across the cornea, a number of dilute detergents were assessed in the eyes of volunteers. Although considered "generally harmless to rabbit eyes", some caused pain and irritation in people. For instance, a detergent called Brij 58 produced "alarming" changes to the surface of the human eye, together with discomfort and blurred vision.[1] In rabbits Brij 58 is classified as a "non-irritant."[2]

A 3% solution of a similar product, Brij 35, caused delayed irritation in volunteers but was also non-irritating to the rabbit eye, even when undiluted.[1] And although another detergent, dupanol, caused immediate severe pain in human subjects,[1] it was considered to have only moderate effects in the eyes of rabbits.[3]

References

1) R.J.Marsh & D.M.Maurice, *Experimental Eye Research*, 1971, vol.11, 43-48.
2) M.Cornelis et al, *ATLA*, 1991, vol.19, 324-336.
3) L.W.Hazleton, *Proceedings of the Scientific Section of the Toilet Goods Association*, 1952, vol.17, 5-9.

TOXIC TREATMENTS

Many cancer patients have suffered unnecessarily because researchers believed large doses of anticancer drugs were necessary for efficient treatment. The widely held view was that to be effective in reducing tumour size, cancer chemotherapy must also be toxic:[1] only then did doctors think they had given sufficient drug. The idea was based on animal experiments [1,2] yet there were early warning signs that patients survived longer when given comparatively non-toxic doses, even though the drugs had a smaller effect on tumour size.[3]

The high dose concept has been challenged by clinical researchers. During the 1960s, a series of statistical studies by the Rosewell Park Memorial Institute for Cancer Research in New York, concluded that toxicity is *not* necessary and can be counterproductive.[2] In 1976, London cancer specialists found that the animal data on which the high dose concept is based, are not always valid for human patients.[1] They argued that "Since patients given large doses of antineoplastic [anticancer] agents are often at greater risk of toxicity, alternative methods of improving the selectivity of cancer chemotherapy must be explored."

References
1) M.H.N.Tattersall & J.S.Tobias, *Lancet*, 1976, November 13, 1073-1074.
2) I.D.Bross, *Perspectives On Animal Research*, 1989, vol.1, 83-108.
3) M.A.Schneiderman & M.J.Krant, *Cancer Chemotherapy Reports*, 1966, vol.50, 107-112.

ANIMALS & AIDS

The fact that even chimpanzees do not develop AIDS when infected with HIV, casts serious doubt on the validity of animal experiments.[1] Some AIDS researchers seem to recognise this since vaccines which failed to protect chimpanzees from infection with HIV, were nevertheless tested in human trials![2] Certainly, faith in animal tests could have serious repercussions. For instance, failure to induce AIDS in laboratory animals has been used to support arguments *against* HIV as the cause.[3]

Attempts to produce "animal models" of AIDS could be dangerous in other ways. By inserting parts of the human immune system into mice, scientists believed they had developed an animal model of AIDS. But fears have been expressed that interaction of HIV with viruses commonly found in mice may not only make the "model" irrelevant to people but promote hazardous changes in the AIDS virus. The new HIV variants could then spread in different ways, possibly even through the air. [4]

References

1) P.Newmark, *Nature*, 1989, October 19, 566-567.
2) A.S.Fauci & P.J.Fischinger, *Public Health Reports*, 1988, vol.103, 230-236.
3) *New Scientist*, 1988, March 3, 34.
4) J.Marx, *Science*, 1990, February 16, 809; P.Lusso et al, *Science*, 1990, February 16, 848-852.

USEFUL THERAPIES AT RISK FROM FALSE ANIMAL DATA

The diuretic drug furosemide is well established in clinical practice as a treatment for cardiovascular and kidney disease. In mice, however, the drug produces massive liver damage. Similar effects have also been found in rats and hamsters.[1] Yet liver toxicity is not a major problem for human patients,[2] and the harmful effects in mice have been traced to a breakdown product of furosemide which is not found to any serious extent in the human body.[3] Fortunately, the effects in mice were reported *after* furosemide's safety in people had been determined.[3] Otherwise the drug may never have been introduced.

A comparison of human and animal test data shows that furosemide is not an isolated example. At most, only one out of every four side-effects predicted by animal tests actually occurs in people.[4] These findings suggest that reliance on animal experiments must lead to the rejection of potentially valuable medicines.

References
1) R.M.Walker & T.F.McElligott, *Journal of Pathology*, 1981, vol.135, 301-314.
2) M.N.G.Dukes in *Meyler's Side Effects of Drugs*, 11th edition, Ed. M.N.G.Dukes (Elsevier, 1988).
3) M.Weatherall, *Nature*, 1982, April 1, 387-390.
4) A.P.Fletcher, *Journal of the Royal Society of Medicine*, 1978, vol.71, 693-698.

TRANSPLANT DRUG CAUSES UNEXPECTED KIDNEY DAMAGE

Cyclosporin is used to prevent rejection of transplanted organs and although hailed as a major advance over existing drugs, it is not a panacea: side-effects are common and sometimes dangerous. The most serious hazard is kidney damage,[1] an effect not predicted by the initial animal tests.[2] Ironically, kidney toxicity has been reported in almost 80% of kidney transplant patients receiving the drug.[2] Some heart transplant patients treated with cyclosporin required dialysis because their kidneys had failed.[3]

Subsequent animal experiments showed that only extremely high doses of cyclosporin could induce kidney toxicity in rats [1] although dogs and rhesus monkeys were still unaffected.[2] Researchers believe that "...failure to produce renal dysfunction [kidney damage] experimentally that is similar to that seen clinically may result from species differences in metabolism."[2]

Although cyclosporin can prevent rejection of transplanted organs in both animals and people, an early review of the drug found sufficient variation in experimental results to suggest that "The immunosuppressive effects of cyclosporin have ...differed considerably between species, limiting any direct inference that may be made regarding use in human organ transplantation..."[1]

References

1) D.J.Cohen et al, *Annals of Internal Medicine*, 1984, vol.101, 667-682.
2) W.M.Bennett & J.P.Pulliam, *Annals of Internal Medicine*, 1983, vol.99, 851-854.
3) *Lancet*, 1986, February 22, 419-420.

ANIMAL TESTS MASK NERVE DAMAGE RISK

In September 1983, the antidepressant zimelidine (Zelmid) was withdrawn worldwide following potentially serious side-effects including nerve damage, leading to loss of sensation or paralysis.[1] Some patients also suffered hypersensitivity reactions such as fever, headache, muscle or joint pains, and liver problems. The drug had been introduced only a year earlier but Britain's Committee on Safety of Medicines had received over 300 reports of adverse reactions, 60 of which were serious: there were 7 deaths.[2] Prolonged tests in rats and dogs had shown no evidence of toxicity at 5 times the human dose.[3]

References

1) B.Blackwell in *Side Effects of Drugs Annual*, vol.8, Eds. M.N.G.Dukes & J.Elis (Elsevier, 1984).
2) R.D.Mann, *Modern Drug Use, an Inquiry on Historical Principles* (MTP Press, 1984).
3) R.C.Heel et al, *Drugs*, 1982, vol.24, 169-206.

COUGH REMEDY LEAVES OVERDOSE PATIENTS IN COMA

In 1984 a Milan Poison Control Centre reported 32 patients with severe neurological side-effects following an overdose of zipeprol, the cough suppressant.[1] Symptoms included seizures and coma, and the Centre stated that "Zipeprol should be much more strictly controlled..." Animal tests had given no warning of severe neurological problems despite the use of higher doses.[2]

References
1) C.Moroni et al, *Lancet*, 1984, January 7, 45.
2) D.Cosnier et al,*Drug Research*, 1976, vol.26, 848-854; G.Rispat et al, *Drug Research*, 1976, vol.26, 523-530.

NINE SPECIES FAIL TO PREDICT LIVER DAMAGE

Evicromil (code name FPL 52757) was submitted for clinical trial as an antiasthmatic drug following safety evaluation in mice, rats, hamsters, rabbits, ferrets, squirrel monkeys, cynomolgus monkeys, stump-tail monkeys and baboons. Despite using doses many times greater than the amount intended for human use, no harmful effects were seen, especially with respect to the liver.[1] Yet 20% of patients participating in the trial had symptoms of liver damage, precluding any further development of the drug.[2] Subsequent tests showed that liver toxicity could only be induced in dogs.[1,2]

References
1) D.V.Parke in *Animals & Alternatives in Toxicity Testing*, Eds. M.Balls et al (Academic Press, 1983).
2) C.T.Eason et al, *Regulatory Toxicology & Pharmacology*, 1990, vol.11, 288-307.

ANIMAL VICTIMS ESCALATE AFTER ICI DRUG FAILS

During clinical trials, ICI's arthritis drug fenclozic acid unexpectedly produced jaundice in some of the patients. Researchers were surprised since tests with rats, mice, dogs and monkeys had given no hint of liver problems.[1] Not content with these results, further experiments with rabbits, guinea pigs, ferrets, cats,pigs,horses,neonatal rats and mice, together with a different strain of rat, were carried out but still no evidence of liver damage could be found.[1] The ICI researcher commented that "The quite unexpected onset of jaundice in a few patients caused withdrawal of the drug from humans and initiated a vast programme of experimental work. This search for hepatotoxicity [liver damage] in different species or any indication of its likelihood has so far been unrewarding."[1]

Reference

1) S.J.Alcock, *Proceedings of the European Society for the Study of Drug Toxicity*, 1971, vol.12, 184-190.

LIVER DAMAGE NOT PREDICTED...AGAIN!

In 1985 Britain's Committee on Safety of Medicines issued a special warning of serious liver damage associated with antifungal drug ketoconazole (Nizeral) [1]. The Committee cited 82 cases with 5 deaths. The warnings followed similar action by the US Food and Drug Administration in 1982.[2] Doctors are advised to monitor their patients carefully and perform regular liver function tests throughout treatment with ketoconazole. No evidence of liver toxicity had been found in the original animal tests.[3]

References

1) *Lancet*, 1985, January 12, 121.
2) C.B.M.Tester-Dalderup in *Meyler's Side-Effects of Drugs,* 11th edition, Ed. M.N.G.Dukes (Elsevier,1988).
3) J.K.Heiberg & E.Svejgaard, *British Medical Journal*, 1981, September 26, 825.

ANIMALS STARVE IN BRAIN RESEARCH FIASCO

Reliance on animal experiments rather than human observations delayed a full realisation that lack of food early in life can harm the brain. During the first quarter of the 20th century, there was considerable interest in the possibility that lack of food during childhood might interfere with the proper development of the brain and therefore affect later achievement of the individual. Unfortunately, almost all the research was carried out on animals and showed that starving baby or adult rats had no effect on the brain. Not surprisingly, the topic was abandoned and only resumed in the late 1950s when children with histories of undernutrition were persistently found to underachieve, both in school and in formal tests.[1]

Researchers then realised that the early animal tests had failed since no account had been taken of the "brain growth spurt". This is the period of fastest growth when the brain is at its most vulnerable. Furthermore, the exact timing varies between the species : in human babies the brain growth spurt begins during the final stage of pregnancy and proceeds through to at least a year; in guinea pigs, it occurs almost entirely during the foetal period; and in rats it happens during the first 3 weeks after birth.[2]

Despite millions of underfed and malnourished *people,*"early life undernutrition" remains a popular subject among *animal* researchers. Unlike current aid levels to developing nations, there seems no shortage of funds for such research : indeed, one justification is that, someday, it might better enable us to give relief to the starving![3]

References
1) J.Dobbing in *Early Nutrition & Later Behaviour*, Ed. J.Dobbing (Academic Press, 1987).
2) J.Dobbing & J.L.Smart, *British Medical Bulletin*, 1974, vol.30, 164-168.
3) J.L.Smart in ref.1.

THE PRACTOLOL SYNDROME

Practolol (Eraldin), marketed by ICI during the early 1970s for the treatment of heart conditions, was "particularly notable for the thoroughness with which its toxicity was studied in animals, to the satisfaction of the regulatory authorities."[1] Nevertheless, unforeseen side-effects began to emerge including serious skin, eye and abdominal problems. Some patients suffered dry eyes, conjunctivitis and corneal damage leading to blindness. There were also cases of stomach damage with obstruction of the intestine, a condition known as sclerosing peritonitis which led to 23 reported deaths.[2] Overall, ICI compensated more than 1000 victims.[3]

The "practolol syndrome" had not been predicted by animal experiments [4] and even after the drug was withdrawn in 1976, no-one could replicate the harmful effects in laboratory animals.[1]

References
1) M.Weatherall, *Nature*, 1982, April 1, 387-390.
2) G.R.Venning, *British Medical Journal*, 1983, January 15, 199-202; January 22, 289-292.
3) *A Question of Balance*, Office of Health Economics, 1980.
4) F.H.Gross & W.H.Inman (Eds.), *Drug Monitoring* (Academic Press,1977).

ANIMALS MISS STEROID EYE RISKS

One of the most serious side-effects of steroid eye therapy is glaucoma. An abnormally high pressure builds up within the eye and can lead to permanent loss of vision if the effects are prolonged. During the early 1950s, when corticosteroids were first employed in ophthalmology, animal tests suggested that cortisone had no effect on pressure within the eye.[1] Subsequent attempts to induce glaucoma in rabbits and monkeys proved difficult or impossible,[2] and researchers at Britain's Porton Down laboratories refer to "the differing response of the eye of man and animals to repeated topical [surface] application of corticosteroids. Such a procedure is without effect on tension of the eye of many experimental mammals, but increases tension in the human eye."[3]

Another side-effect of steroid therapy that is difficult to replicate in laboratory animals is cataract. Although scientists have produced slight changes in the lens of the rabbit's eye after repeated application of high doses, they did not mimic the more serious condition found in human patients.[2]

References

1) L.H.Leopold et al, *American Journal of Ophthalmology*, 1951, vol.34, 361-371.
2) W.M.Grant,*Toxicology of the Eye*,2nd edition,(Charles Thomas, 1974).
3) B.Ballantyne & D.W.Swanston in *Current Approaches in Toxicology*, Ed. B.Ballantyne (Wright & Sons, 1977).

BABIES AT RISK FROM TALC

In 1991, doctors at Southampton General Hospital warned that inhaling babies' talcum powder could be fatal,[1] representing "an unappreciated hazard." They state that "talcum powder can cause severe respiratory symptoms in infants: its use should be discouraged and containers should carry a warning and have child proof caps." Eight deaths have been attributed to inhalation of talc.

Concerns over the safety of talc have been raised before and studies of talc miners and millers have shown that it can damage the lungs.[2] But experiments in which huge amounts of the commercial product were administered to animals, seemed to suggest no hazard to consumers. For instance, in 1977 experimenters exposed hamsters to high grade cosmetic talc at doses nearly *2000 times* higher than that experienced by babies during toilet care. There was no effect on survival or damage to the lungs.[3] In the same year, other scientists forced rats to breathe talc at doses approaching 6000 times those used in baby care. Despite the massive amounts, there was only a slight effect on the lungs.[3]

References
1) P.W.Pairaudean et al, *British Medical Journal*, 1991, May 18, 1200-1201.
2) A.Seaton in *Occupational Lung Diseases*, eds. W.K.Morgan & A.Seaton (Saunders, 1982).
3) *Lancet*, 1977, June 25, 1348-1349.

ANIMAL TESTS MINIMISE RIOT GAS HAZARD

Studies with human volunteers have shown that animal experiments can seriously underestimate the likely effect of riot control gases on the eye. The tests found that people are 18 times more sensitive to CS than rabbits, and 90 times more sensitive to another sensory irritant, CR.[1]

When applied to the rabbit's eye, a solution of CR produced only "minor transient changes" in pressure within the eye. But instillation of a *smaller* amount into the human eye produced a 40% rise in pressure within 5 minutes compared with only a 3% rise after 10 minutes in rabbits.[2]

Species differences have also been found when CS and CR are applied to the skin. A method known as the human blister-base technique allows volunteers to classify irritants according to the level of discomfort they produce. The procedure showed that CR is a more potent irritant than CS which is confirmed by other human test systems, yet is the *reverse* of that found from experiments on rodents.[3] The study also found that a further sensory irritant, VAN, is less potent than CR which is again the opposite of that found from animal tests. In a masterpiece of understatement, the researchers conclude that "data derived from humans thus appears to be of importance when assessing irritant potency."[3]

References

1) D.W.Swanston in *Animals & Alternatives in Toxicity Testing*, Eds. M.Balls et al (Academic Press, 1983).
2) B.Ballantyne et al in *Current Approaches in Toxicology*, Ed. B.Ballantyne (Wright & Sons, 1977).
3) R.W.Foster et al, *Pain*, 1986, vol.25, 269-278.

LAB RATS RAISE FALSE FEARS OVER WATER TREATMENT

Widespread fluoridation is thought to be a key factor in the decline of dental caries, and originated from a dentist's observation that children with mottled teeth, caused by a naturally high concentration of fluoride in the water supply, seemed to have less tooth decay than usual.[1] Although fluoride has been added to public water supplies for over 3 decades with apparently no ill effects,[2] experiments with laboratory rats raised concerns that it may cause cancer.[3] The findings prompted an in-depth analysis of over 50 human health studies conducted over the previous 40 years. The resulting report by America's Department of Health and Human Services (DHHS) found no evidence of a link with cancer and gave fluoride the "all-clear".

Animal tests have indicated other harmful effects of fluoride but the DHHS report notes that sensitivity to fluoride varies widely between species, making results difficult to apply to humans.[4]

References

1) A.M.Lilienfield & D.A.Lilienfield, *Foundations of Epidemiology* (Oxford University Press, 1980).
2) Eg. see R.Peto & R.Doll, *The Causes of Cancer* (Oxford University Press, 1981).
3) *Journal of NIH Research*, 1991, vol.3, 46.
4) C.Anderson, *Nature*, 1991, February 28, 732.

NATURAL FLAVOURING BANNED AFTER MISLEADING ANIMAL DATA

Coumarin is a naturally occurring product derived from the Tonka bean and has been employed for over 100 years. It is used in consumer products and as a therapeutic agent, for instance in the treatment of cancer and infectious disease. During the 1950s, doubt was cast on coumarin's safety when experiments produced liver damage in laboratory rats. As a result, coumarin was banned as a food flavouring agent.[1]

Subsequent research, however, showed wide species variation in response to coumarin. While dogs also suffer liver toxicity, there are only minimal effects in baboons.[2] And doses which damage the rat's liver are harmless to gerbils.[1] Even different strains of the same species react differently and coumarin is less harmful to the DBA/2J strain of laboratory mouse than the CH3/HeJ strain.[3]

Among patients receiving relatively high doses of coumarin for therapeutic purposes, liver toxicity is said to be "very rare",[1] and rats and dogs are now considered poor "models" for assessing the drug because they metabolise coumarin in a completely different way.[1,2,3]

References
1) J.H.Fentem et al, *Toxicology*, 1992, vol.71, 129-136.
2) J.G.Evans et al, *Food & Cosmetic Toxicology*, 1979, vol.17, 187-193.
3) W.Endell & G.Seidel, *Agents & Actions*, 1978, vol.8, 299-302.

INHALATION TESTS THROW FALSE DOUBT ON FORMALDEHYDE

Fears for the safety of formaldehyde workers followed reports that the chemical causes cancer in rats.[1] Formaldehyde is widely used as a laboratory fixative and as an embalming fluid but human epidemiological studies had revealed no evidence of cancer. The animal tests led to further observations of exposed workers but these were also negative.[1]

The rats had been forced to breathe such high doses (7-15 times that inhaled by workers) that the formaldehyde caused tissue damage which led to the cancers. Nevertheless, "...there are still some who believe that the positive results in the rat are the dominant factor to be taken into account and overrides the epidemiology but there is always some hope that common sense may prevail." [1]

Reference

1) P.Grasso, *Journal of the Royal Society of Medicine*, 1989, vol.82, 470-473.

EPILEPSY 'MODELS' GIVE FITFUL RESULTS

Scientists have devised more than 50 ways of inducing fits in laboratory animals. One reason for the large number is that "none of the models is fully trustworthy as an imitation of clinical epilepsy,"[1] and indeed results can vary depending on the "model" chosen.

An example is the artificial sweetener aspartame. In research sponsored by the NutraSweet Company and the Wellcome Trust, researchers at London's Institute of Psychiatry carried out experiments with photosensitive baboons in which fits are induced by flashing lights. The tests followed suggestions that high doses of aspartame may produce seizures in sensitive people. Aspartame had no effect in the baboons but conflicting data has been found in other animal models: aspartame enhances chemically-induced convulsions in mice, for instance, but has no effect on electric shock-induced or sound-induced seizures in these animals.[2]

Similar species differences are found in drug development. Although reducing convulsions in mice and baboons, the drug THIP proved ineffective when tried in patients with epilepsy.[3]

References
1) R.S.Fisher, *Brain Research Reviews*, 1989, vol.14, 245-278.
2) B.S.Meldrum et al, *Epilepsy Research*, 1989, vol.4, 1-7.
3) *Lancet*, 1985, January 26, 198-200.

WORKERS AT RISK FROM MISLEADING ANIMAL TESTS

In 1991 the US Occupational Safety and Health Administration decided that glass fibre products should be labelled as a potential cancer hazard.[1] The decision followed studies of glass fibre workers that showed an increased risk of lung cancer.

Glass wool products have been manufactured for about 60 years during which animal experiments seemed reassuring. In the 1950s, experiments with rats, guinea pigs, rabbits and monkeys produced no lung damage when the animals were forced to breathe the fibres.[2] And an analysis of further tests conducted during the 1980s noted that "An increase in lung tumours or mesothelioma has not been observed following long-term inhalation studies in several animal species including rats, hamsters, guinea pigs, mice, monkeys, and baboons exposed to glass fibres, glass wool or mineral wool."[3]

Ironically, experiments in which rats did develop cancer have been dismissed as unlikely to have any relevance to the human condition. This is because the glass fibres were artificially implanted into the tissue membrane lining the animal's lung, whereas in people the usual means of exposure is through breathing. Furthermore, it is well known that rats are especially prone to cancer when solid substances are surgically implanted into their bodies.[2] In his book *Occupational Lung Disorders*, Raymond Parkes concludes that "the production of malignant tumours in animals by direct implantation experiments is unlikely to have any relevance to human exposure."

References
1) Letter from G.F.Scannell, Assistant Secretary for Occupational Safety and Health, Washington DC, to Richard Munson, Chairman of Victims of Fibreglass (May 6,1991); *The Guardian*, July 20, 1991.
2) Reported in R.Parkes, *Occupational Lung Disorders* (Butterworths, 1982).
3) C.S.Wheeler, *Toxicology & Industrial Health*, 1990, vol.6, 293-307.

DOG DEATHS DENY WOMEN CONTRACEPTIVE OPTION

During the 1960s, doctors noticed that women receiving the steroid drug Depo-Provera as a treatment for premature labour, experienced a delay in the return of fertility after the birth of their babies. The observation led to clinical trials of the drug as a possible long-acting contraceptive.[1] Injectable preparations of Depo-Provera are now known to bυ as effective as oral contraceptives and are available in Europe, Asia, Africa and the Far East. In America however, approval was delayed for many years.[2]

Much of the controversy surrounding Depo-Provera relates to experiments with beagle dogs that indicated a host of disturbing side-effects.[2] There were abnormal growth problems, cases of breast cancer, and many animals died of pyometra, a condition in which pus accumulates in the uterus. None of these effects have been observed in women taking Depo-Provera[1,2] and scientists point to physiological differences between human beings and dogs which make beagles especially sensitive to certain kinds of steroids.[1]

High doses of Depo-Provera can also cause cancer in monkeys but again their relevance has been questioned since the tumours arise from a type of cell not found in women. Furthermore, the kind of cancer produced in monkeys is successfully *treated* by Depo-Provera in women![1]

In 1991 an editorial in the *Lancet* entitled "DMPA [Depo-Provera] and breast cancer: the dog has had its day", argued that "Countries such as the USA, Australia and Japan would do well to reassess their existing policies on injectable preparations, otherwise they may deprive their female citizens of a reliable, effective and safe method of contraception."[2] One year later, America's Food & Drug Administration finally decided to approve Depo-Provera as a long-acting contraceptive.

References

1) *Bulletin of the World Health Organisation,* 1982, vol.60, 199-210.
2) *Lancet,* 1991, October 5, 856-857.

USELESS TREATMENT POISONS WORKERS

In 1939, animal researchers devised an astonishing treatment for silicosis, the debilitating lung disease caused by exposure to silica dust. They found that inhalation of metallic aluminium could prevent silicosis in laboratory rabbits,[1] and from the early 1940s to the mid-1950s, the technique was widely employed by industry in an attempt to treat or prevent the condition amongst workers.[2]

Before beginning work, men whose occupations exposed them to silica, passed through an aluminium dusting chamber where they breathed a daily dose of the powder. But in 1956, studies of pottery workers showed that the method did not work and the Industrial Pulmonary Disease Committee of Britain's Medical Research Council recommended that the technique should not be used.[3]

Today we know that the treatment itself carried risks. Although large doses of aluminium proved harmless to animals,[4] cases of lung damage and cancer have been reported amongst aluminium workers.[5] Furthermore, studies of Canadian miners who breathed aluminium powder to prevent silicosis, have revealed symptoms consistent with the current theory that aluminium may cause Alzheimer's Disease![6]

References

1) J.J.Denny et al, *Canadian Medical Association Journal,* 1939, vol.40, 213: reported in ref.3.
2) W.R.Parkes, *Occupational Lung Disorders* (Butterworths,1982).
3) M.C.S.Kennedy, *British Journal of Industrial Medicine,* 1956, vol.13, 85-101.
4) L.U.Gardner et al, *Journal of Industrial Hygiene & Toxicology,* 1944, vol.26, 211-223.
5) M.J.Ellenhorn & D.G.Barceloux, *Medical Toxicology* (Elsevier, 1988).
6) Lord Walton of Detchant, *Journal of the Royal Society of Medicine,* 1992, vol.85, 69-70.

POISONING TESTS OFFER LITTLE HOPE TO OVERDOSE PATIENTS

For decades animals have been deliberately poisoned to death in lethal dose (LD50) toxicity tests, yet the results are of little value in the prevention and treatment of overdose patients and can be misleading.[1] According to their lethal doses in rats, aspirin would seem safer than another common pain killing drug,ibuprofen. In fact, human overdose experience reveals that ibuprofen is the safer drug.[1] As physicians at London's National Poisons Centre point out, "The 'natural experiment' of cases of self poisoning has to be taken as the starting point as the results of experiments on animals cannot reliably be extrapolated to man..." [2]

References
1) G.N.Volans in *The Contribution of Acute Toxicity Tests to the Evaluation of Pharmaceuticals*, Eds. D.Schuppan et al (Springer-Verlag, Berlin, 1986).
2) S.Cassidy & J.Henry, *British Medical Journal*, 1987, October 24, 1021-1024.

ANIMAL DIET STUDIES CONTRADICT HUMAN COLON CANCER RISKS

Comparisons of people living in different countries, together with other human studies, have shown that too much fat in the diet can lead to cancer of the colon, with *saturated* fat the chief culprit. Animal tests agree that too much fat can be dangerous but suggest it is the *polyunsaturated* fats that are mostly to blame.[1]

Clinical studies have also suggested that a high fibre diet is beneficial and the idea has been tested by animal researchers. Again the results are conflicting, some experiments showing a reduced risk of cancer and others an increased risk.[2] And although population studies have identified diets high in animal protein as most risky,[3] much laboratory research suggests that the type of protein is irrelevant.[2]

Human studies have consistently shown that diets rich in fruit and vegetables can protect against colon cancer. In contrast, many of the natural substances evolved by fruit and vegetables to protect themselves from predators and parasites, actually *cause* cancer when tested in rats and mice![4]

References

1) J.L.Freudenheim & S.Graham, *Epidemiologic Reviews*, 1989, vol.11, 229-235.
2) D.Galloway, *Cancer Surveys*, 1989, vol.8, 169-188.
3) B.Armstrong & R.Doll, *International Journal of Cancer*, 1975, vol.15, 617-631.
4) P.H.Abelson, *Science*, 1990, September 21, 1357.

CANCER CURE DELAYED BY FALSE ANIMAL DATA

Although prednisone is a valuable drug for the treatment of leukemia and other human cancers, it fails to work in a range of animal tumours including two different types of leukemia in mice.[1] Ironically, these experimental cancers were once commonly used by America's National Cancer Institute in attempts to identify promising new drugs!

Prednisone can be even more effective when used in conjunction with certain other anticancer drugs but once again animal tests have proved misleading: of 6 drug combinations showing an improved clinical effect, only one was correctly predicted by animal experiments.[1]

The incentive to develop prednisone stemmed from encouraging results with the closely related steroid, cortisone, a hormone derived from the adrenal gland. In 1930 Californian physicians claimed they had cured human cancers with extracts of adrenal gland. Unfortunately, these findings led to *animal* rather than human trials and when the former proved negative, the treatment was abandoned.[2] Only when the tests were repeated, a decade later, did researchers confirm that adrenal extracts could be beneficial against some forms of cancer. Promising human trials led to the development of analogues such as prednisone.

References
1) R.J.Johnson & A.Goldin, *Cancer Treatment Reviews*, 1975, vol.2, 1-31.
2) B.Reines, *Cancer Research on Animals: Impact and Alternatives* (NAVS, Chicago, 1986).

MONKEY EXPERIMENTS DELAY POLIO BREAKTHROUGH

Pro-vivisection organisations often cite the conquest of polio as a triumph of animal experiments. In fact, emphasis on animal research rather than human studies delayed a proper understanding of the disease for over 25 years.[1]

In 1908 Landsteiner and Popper announced they had discovered the polio virus: tissue from an infected patient who had died produced spinal cord disease when injected into two monkeys. The animals died with one developing paralysis in both legs. Negative results had been obtained with rabbits, guinea pigs and mice and indeed the researchers had been "fortunate" in choosing Old World monkeys such as the rhesus who are highly susceptible to the disease. New World monkeys are relatively resistant.

Although obviously important to discover the virus, the means by which it was achieved had a devastating impact on polio research. Believing they now had an exact replica of the human infection, scientists focussed their main attention on the artificially induced disease in monkeys. Based on these experiments it was generally believed that poliovirus enters the body through the nose and that it only attacks the central nervous system (CNS) producing spinal cord damage.[1,2.]

Yet by 1907 careful epidemiological analysis of actual human cases had shown that poliomyelitis was not entirely or even chiefly a disease of the CNS. The studies, based on over 1000 Swedish cases, were carried out by Dr. Ivar Wickman, who also correctly concluded that the gastrointestinal tract was the probable route of infection.[1] By 1912 other clinical studies also established the intestinal tract as the means of infection.

Tragically, animal experiments so dominated research that prior to 1937 most scientists rejected the notion that polio is an intestinal disease. As Dr Paul explains in *A History of Poliomyelitis*, "...with the discovery of the virus and the rush of enthusiasm for experimental work, the mainstream had soon been diverted away from Wickman's correct concepts of the human disease gained from clinical epidemiological work carried out so painstakingly in the field."

Whether the virus entered the body by the mouth or nose was of great practical importance, for it determined strategies for preventing the spread of disease. By 1937 researchers had produced a nasal spray that prevented infection in monkeys. It was widely promoted for human use but inevitably failed.[1] The only result was to abolish the children's sense of smell, in some cases permanently.[2]

Support for the nasal route of infection gradually waned after further clinical observations while animal researchers were no doubt reassured with the finding that chimpanzees, unlike the rhesus monkeys used earlier, could be infected via the intestinal tract. It was only when scientists understood that poliovirus enters the mouth and first resides in the intestines that it was possible to develop an orally administered vaccine, and this formed the basis of Sabin's approach.

For years, monkeys were also used for diagnostic purposes, to test for the presence of virus. Tissue samples from patients (or other monkeys) were innoculated into the animals who were then assessed for damage to the spinal cord. The procedure was laborious, time consuming and expensive but during the early years of the 20th century, scientists had only learnt to grow viruses in living animals. However, in 1949 Enders, Weller and Robbins showed that polio virus could be grown in human tissue culture. Most significantly, the virus produced a specific change in the infected cells which could be recognised under the microscope. It was therefore easy to detect the presence of polio virus in tissue samples. Had such a quick and simple alternative been introduced at an earlier stage, progress would surely have been more rapid. Indeed, by suggesting that virus would only grow in the CNS, the misleading monkey model of polio delayed the development of tissue culture techniques which were ultimately critical to the discovery of a vaccine.[1,3]

References

1) J.R.Paul, *A History of Poliomyelitis* (Yale University Press,1971).
2) H.F.Dowling, *Fighting Infection* (Harvard University Press, 1977).
3) *A Critical Look at Animal Research* (Medical Research Modernization Committee, New York, 1990).

ANTIBIOTICS, GUINEA PIGS & HAMSTERS

Years of experimentation have taught scientists that guinea pigs and hamsters are especially sensitive to the harmful effects of antibiotics. For instance, widely prescribed human antibiotics such as ampicillin, amoxycillin and oxytetracycline are considered "toxic" and therefore inappropriate for use in these species.[1] Another example is erythromycin where the usually recommended human dose is enough to *kill* a hamster![2]

Today, "it is generally recognised that the guinea pig is peculiarly sensitive to the lethal effects of antibiotics,"[3] but this was not always realised. In his book *Drug Development: From Laboratory to Clinic*, Dr Walter Sneader describes how "it was fortunate that Florey and Chain did not decide to use guinea pigs when first testing penicillin, for they may then have abandoned the project as these animals are hypersensitive to penicillin." Florey and Chain were the Oxford scientists who carried out animal tests following Fleming's discovery of penicillin. Florey later commented "...mice were tried in the initial toxicity tests because of their small size, but what a lucky chance it was, for in this respect man is like the mouse and not the guinea pig. If we had used guinea pigs exclusively we should have said that penicillin was toxic, and we probably should not have proceeded to try to overcome the difficulties of producing the substance for trial in man."[4]

References

1) A.A.Tuffery (ed.), *Laboratory Animals - An Introduction for New Experimenters* (Wiley, 1987).
2) A single, minimum recommended dose of erythromycin is 250-500mg every 6 hours i.e. 3.5-7.0 mg/kg for a 70kg person. The lethal dose for hamsters is 3.5mg/kg (ref.3)
3) S.J.Desalva et al, *Toxicology & Applied Pharmacology*, 1969, vol.14, 510-514.
4) H.Florey, *Conquest*, January, 1953.

ANIMALS DIVERT ATTENTION FROM CANCER PREVENTION

Prevention is always better than cure, particularly for diseases like cancer where treatment can be both difficult and unpleasant. But first, doctors must discover the causes so people know how to avoid ill-health. This is the primary role of epidemiology - the study of disease in human populations. Tragically, a preference for laboratory research and animal experiments diverted attention from epidemiology, and for decades little was known about the main causes of human cancer.

Before World War I, epidemiology had identified several causes of the disease.[1] For instance, pipe smokers were more likely to develop cancer of the lip; workers in the aniline dye industry often contracted bladder cancer; and skin cancer was an occupational hazard of radiologists. It was also known that combustion products of coal (soot and tar) could cause the disease, an observation dating back to 1775 when the English surgeon Potts identified soot as a carcinogen in chimney sweeps.

Attempts to replicate Potts' findings in laboratory animals repeatedly failed[2] but finally, in 1918, Japanese researchers reported that cancer could be produced on a rabbit's ear by continually painting it with tar, a discovery that changed the course of cancer research. According to the renowned British epidemiologist Sir Richard Doll, human observational data were now commonly dismissed because it was confidentally assumed that laboratory experiments held the key to success.[1] Crucial epidemiological studies like those of Percy Stocks at London University, who reported in 1933 that people consuming larger amounts of fruit and vegetables were less likely to develop cancer,[3] received little attention,[1] yet today we know that Stocks was right.[4]

The absence of human epidemiological data allowed mistaken ideas based on animal research to flourish. Although we now know that only about 5% of Western cancers are linked to viral infection,[5] some scientists believed that most, if not all cases were caused by viruses, a view derived from experiments on animals where it is easy to transmit the disease in this way.[6] One animal researcher even argued that women should not breast feed their babies: he believed that in humans,as in mice, a virus is the prime cause of breast cancer, and that the virus is acquired in the mother's milk![7]

Following World War II, interest in epidemiology was reawakened with the striking discovery that smoking causes lung cancer. This breakthrough led to further population studies which identified the causes of many other types of cancer. The result is that 80-90% of cases are now considered potentially preventable. And it is revealing that the 1980 US Congress Office of Technology Assessment Report on the causes of cancer, relied far more on epidemiology than laboratory tests because these "cannot provide reliable risk assessments." [5]

References
1) R.Doll, *Cancer*, 1980, vol.45, 2475-2485.
2) W.H.Woglom, *Archives of Pathology*, 1926, vol.2, 533-576.
3) P.Stocks & M.N.Karn, *Annals of Eugenics*, 1933, vol.5, 237-280.
4) J.Robbins, *Diet for a New America* (Stillpoint, 1987).
5) R.Peto & R.Doll, *The Causes of Cancer* (Oxford University Press, 1981).
6) E.Northrup, *Science Looks at Smoking* (Conard-McCann, 1957).
7) J.Furth, *Bulletin of the New York Academy of Medicine*, 1964, vol.40,421-431.

THE DOGMA OF DEATH

In a meticulous study at the Vienna General Hospital, Ignaz Phillipe Semmelweiss discovered that expectant mothers were more likely to die of childbed (puerperal) fever if their attendants had previously been working in the dissecting and post-mortem rooms. The disease, he reasoned, must be caused by an infection carried from the dissecting room on the hands of doctors and students. When Semmelweiss insisted on strict hygiene, the death rate promptly dropped from 1 in 8 confinements to 1 in 100.[1]

Tragically, the Hospital professors responded with such hostility that Semmelweiss was forced to leave. Only 4 years earlier, in 1843, the American researcher and humanitarian Oliver Wendell Holmes had reached the same conclusion by careful observation, but had been similarly villified. According to medical statistician Dr Sigmund Peller, "In a world that had not been stultified by the idea that only animal experimentation and only the laboratory can provide proof in matters of human pathology, the battle against puerperal fever would not have needed to wait for the discovery of cocci [the responsible bacterium,discovered during the 1860s]. The experts who, during the 1840s, opposed and prevented the initiation of a rational programme for combatting the disease should have been charged with a negligence that resulted in mass killings. But they were not."[2]

Proper recognition of Semmelweiss and Holmes, and the central role of cleanliness, would surely have hastened the introduction of life-saving, hygenic measures in surgery. But these had to wait at least another 20 years until Lister developed his antiseptic techniques.

References
1) R.Sand, *The Advance to Social Medicine* (Staple Press, 1952)
2) S.Peller, *Quantitative Research in Human Biology* (J.Wright & Sons, 1967).

THE OPREN AFFAIR

The arthritis drug Opren (Oraflex in the US) was withdrawn from the world market in August 1982 following British reports of deaths and serious liver damage in people taking the drug.[1] Since 1980, when Opren was first introduced in the UK, there had been 3,500 reports of harmful effects with 61 deaths, mainly in elderly patients.[2]

Scientists list Opren as a drug whose injuries were not predictable from animal tests,[3] and note that "despite searching preclinical animal toxicity studies...administration to rheumatoid patients resulted in adverse reactions including onycholysis [nail damage] and skin phototoxicity [light sensitivity] and finally in fatal hepatotoxicity [liver damage] whereupon the drug was withdrawn." And Dista, the subsiduary of Eli Lilly who marketed the drug in Britain, stated in their literature that "the effects of benoxaprofen [Opren] in the rhesus monkey were studied for one year...There were no apparent adverse effects on survival."

Researchers believe that the fatal cases of liver damage might have been averted by more extensive clinical trials,[3] especially in the elderly who take much longer to eliminate Opren from the body than either young people or laboratory animals.

References
1) E.M.B.Sorensen, *Toxicology Letters*, 1986, vol.34, 277-286.
2) *British Medical Journal*, 1982. August 14, 459-460.
3) C.T.Eason et al, *Regulatory Toxicology & Pharmacology*, 1990, vol.11, 288-307.

LABORATORY ANIMALS FAIL STROKE VICTIMS

Following experiments on rabbits, dogs, gerbils and monkeys, animal researchers suggested that barbiturates could provide protection against the effects of a stroke.[1] In human stroke victims, however, barbiturates had little or no protective effect.[2] This failure of animal tests is not an isolated example: between 1978 and 1988, 25 drugs were found useful in treating animals with artificially-induced stroke yet none has come into general clinical use.[2]

Stroke researchers are divided over the relevance of animal experiments[3] and some argue that "over-reliance upon such [animal] models may impede rather than advance scientific progress in the treatment of this disease... Each time one of these potential treatments is observed to be effective based upon animal research, it propagates numerous further animal and human studies consuming enormous amounts of time and effort to prove that the observation has little or no relevance to human disease or that it may have been an artifact of the animal model itself."[2]

Although defending the role of animal experiments, researchers at the Mayo Clinic conclude that "Ultimately... the answers to many of our questions regarding the underlying pathophysiology and treatment of stroke do not lie with continued attempts to model the human situation perfectly in animals but rather with the development of techniques to enable the study of...living humans."[2]

References
1) *Stroke*, 1975, vol.6, 28-33; *Stroke*, 1974, vol.5, 1-7;*Neurology*, 1975, vol.25, 870-874; *Stroke*, 1972, vol.3, 726-732; *Annals of Neurology*, 1979, vol.5, 59-64.
2) D.O.Wiebers et al, *Stroke*, 1990, vol.21, 1-3.
3) C.Millikan, *Stroke*, 1992, vol.23, 795-797.

'FLEXIBLE' ANIMAL TESTS SUPPORT RIVAL THEORIES

A new animal test raised fears that Astra's ulcer treatment, omeprazole, may cause stomach cancer. In the test, developed by Glaxo pharmaceutical company, rats are dosed with the suspect drug or chemical, after which tissue samples are removed from the animal's stomach and analysed for effects on DNA, the substance which controls proper development of the cells. Interferance with DNA is regarded as a possible first step to cancer.

The experiments showed that omeprazole damaged the DNA but that ranitidine, Glaxo's own antiulcer drug, did not.[1] On the basis of these results, Glaxo halted comparative clinical trials of ranitidine (Zantac) and omeprazole, an action, according to the *Lancet*, that seemed certain to influence prescribing habits.[2]

In response, Astra, the makers of omeprazole, argued that "the method used by Glaxo is scientifically unsound and the results therefore have no clinical consequences."[3] They noted that "long term studies in which omeprazole was administered for up to 2 years in rats, 18 months in mice, and 1 year in dogs yielded no evidence for a direct carcinogenic potential, in the stomach or elsewhere."

References
1) B.Burlinson et al, *Lancet*, 1990, Fenruary 17, 419.
2) *Lancet*, 1990, February 17, 386.
3) L.Ekman et al, *Lancet*, 1990, February 17, 419-420.

HEART DRUGS MAY HAVE KILLED 3,000

A US study has found that two drugs designed to prevent irregular heart beats can actually *cause* heart attacks in certain types of patient. The cardiac arrhythmia suppression trial (CAST) began in June 1987 but was halted in April 1989 when doctors found more deaths among patients treated with encainide and flecainide than in those receiving a placebo (dummy pill).[1] Based on the findings it has been estimated that, nationwide, 3000 people may have died prematurely after taking the drugs.[2]

In contrast, the animal research had indicated that encainide and flecainide were both safe and effective.[3]

References

1) CAST Investigators, *New England Journal of Medicine*, 1989, August 10, 406-412.
2) Dr. J.Morganroth reported in *Washington Times*, 1989, July 26.
3) Flecainide: B.Holmes & R.C.Heel, *Drugs,* 1985, vol.29, 1-33; encainide: D.C.Harrison et al, *American Heart Journal,* 1980, Vol.100, 1046-1054, and J.E.Byrne et al, *Journal of Pharmacology & Experimental Therapeutics*, 1977, vol.200, 147-154.

RATS CAST DOUBT ON OLIVE OIL!

Although olive oil has been used to anoint the human body for thousands of years without any apparent ill effects,[1] tests carried out at New York University showed that olive oil actually had a *harmful* effect when applied to the skin of rats, causing swelling, proliferation of cells and a great shedding of large, loose flakes of skin![2]

References
1) M.M.Rieger & G.W.Battista, *Journal of the Society of Cosmetic Chemists*, 1964, vol.15, 161-172.
2) E.O.Butcher, *Journal of Investigative Dermatology*, 1951, vol.16, 85-90.

BLEACH HIGHLIGHTS FAULTY SKIN TESTS

Rabbits and guinea pigs are commonly used to assess irritancy but neither provides an accurate model for human skin.[1] For instance,by the criterion of animal experiments, hypochlorite bleach should be considered comparatively safe for human use, since it only produces "slight visible irritation" in rabbits and guinea pigs.[1] However, in human volunteers bleach causes *severe* skin reactions.

Reference

1) G.A.Nixon et al, *Toxicology & Applied Pharmacology*, 1975, vol.31, 481-490.

SMOKING DANGERS MASKED BY FALSE ANIMAL DATA

In 1954, Richard Doll and Bradford Hill published their famous investigation into the smoking habits of British doctors which clearly revealed that the chances of developing lung cancer increased with the number of cigarettes smoked.[1] More than a dozen similar (human) studies had already been published but some scientists still argued that the link between smoking and lung cancer was unwarranted since no-one had produced the disease in laboratory animals.[2]

Two years after publication of Doll and Hill's findings, the British Empire Cancer Campaign - the forerunner of today's Cancer Research Campaign - reported nearly two years of experiments during which mice, rabbits and other animals were exposed to tobacco derivatives by direct inhalation, feeding, injection into the lungs, and skin painting. None developed cancer.[3] And in 1957, American pathologist Eric Northrup concluded in his book *Science Looks at Smoking* that the "....inability to induce experimental cancers, except in a handful of cases, during 50 years of trying, casts serious doubt on the validity of the cigarette-lung cancer theory."

Health warnings were delayed for years and Northrup describes how "it is reassuring...that public health agencies have rejected the demand for a mass lay educational programme against the alleged dangers of smoking. Not one of the leading insurance companies, who consider health hazards in terms of monetary risk, has raised the life insurance rates for heavy smokers."

Despite years of further experimentation, it has proved "difficult or impossible" to induce lung cancer in animals using the method (inhalation) by which people are exposed to the smoke.[4]

References

1) R.Doll and A.B.Hill, *British Medical Journal*, 1954, June 26, 1451-1455.
2) Reported in S.Peller, *Quantitative Research in Human Biology* (J.Wright & Sons, 1967).
3) Reported in E.Northrup, *Science Looks at Smoking* (Conard-McCann, 1957).
4) *Lancet*, 1977, June 25, 1348-1349. See also F.T.Gross et al, *Health Physics*, 1989, vol.56, 256.

TRAGEDY OF THE KILLER DUST

Asbestosis, the lung disease caused by inhaling asbestos, was first recognised in 1907. The reports were so disturbing that 11 years later, the Prudential Insurance Company in New York refused to issue life policies on asbestos workers. Animal research began in 1925 but much of the early experimentation proved contradictory. For instance, during the 1930s, one group of scientists wrongly classified the chrysotile, amosite and crocidolite forms of asbestos as harmless on the basis of animal tests.[1] Others found that chrysotile caused lung damage in guinea pigs but not rabbits.[2]

In 1931 and again in 1951, experimenters reported that the injuries caused by asbestos start to heal when the animals are removed from the dusty atmosphere.[2] This is contrary to human experience where asbestosis *progresses* even when workers are no longer exposed. Only later were researchers able to mimic this aspect of the disease in animals.[3]

The fact that asbestos could harm the lungs was serious enough but doctors soon discovered a more alarming threat - cancer. The first reports of an association between asbestos and lung cancer came from America, England and Germany during the 1930s following examination of people who had died with asbestosis. But attempts to induce cancer in animals repeatedly failed and despite further evidence from exposed workers, the carcinogenic action of asbestos was doubted until the 1960s.[4,5] Only then were researchers able to mimic the disease in animals.

Prior to this "...a large literature on experimental studies has failed to furnish any definate evidence for induction of malignant tumours in animals exposed to various varieties and preparations of asbestos by inhalation or intratracheal injection."[6]

References

1) Reported in L.U.Gardner, *Journal of the American Medical Association*, 1938, November 19, 1925-1936.

2) J.C.Wagner, *British Journal of Industrial Medicine*, 1963, vol.20, 1-12

3) J.C.Wagner et al, *British Journal of Cancer*, 1974, vol.29, 252-269.

4) P.E.Enterline in *Epidemiology & Health Risk Assessment*, Ed. L.Gordis (Oxford University Press, 1988).

5) P.E.Enterline, *American Review of Respiratory Diseases*, 1978, vol.118, 975-978.

6) W.E.Smith et al, *Annals of the New York Academy of Sciences*, 1965, vol.132, 456-488.

TRANSPLANT RESEARCH MISDIRECTED

The key problem for transplant scientists has always been to overcome the body's natural defence mechanism whereby a transplanted organ is rejected. Most of the animal research directed towards this end has relied on rodents, with rats by far the most commonly used species.[1] Yet scientists have discovered important tissue differences which mean their results are of questionable relevance to people, and could be misleading.

For instance, if experiments with rats were used as a guide, patients receiving heart or kidney grafts would only need a very brief period of immunosuppression with drugs like cyclosporin, after which they would never reject their new organ.[2,3] In fact, such a course would be disastrous, for unlike rats, human patients need *lifelong* immunosuppression to prevent organ rejection.

The reason, scientists suspect, is that within a few days of transplantation, the rat's kidney has no cells to stimulate the immune system, so the animal does not reject a transplant when immunosuppressive drug treatment is stopped. In contrast, the human kidney does have these cells as an integral part of its structure and transplant patients must therefore have lifelong drug treatment to suppress the cells' immune-stimulating effects.[4]

During the 1960s and 1970s much research focussed on rat "models" of kidney and heart transplants, and according to John Fabre of Oxford University's Nuffield Department of Surgery, "The many encouraging results raised hopes that a major advance in clinical immunosuppression for transplantation was in the offing, but these hopes have now faded and nothing of the great mass of work has been translated into clinical practice." Fabre suggests that the tissue differences between people and rats may be responsible.[2]

References

1) According to British figures for 1986, 66% of experiments performed in transplant research used rats, 26% used mice, 7% used rabbits, dogs, primates or other species. Source: *Statistics of Experiments on Living Animals, Great Britain, 1986* (HMSO,1987)

2) J.W.Fabre, *Transplantation,* 1982, vol.34, 223-224.

3) D.J.Cohen et al, *Annals of Internal Medicine,* 1984, vol.101, 667-682.

4) P.J.Morris (Ed.), *Tissue Transplantation* (Churchill Livingstone, 1982). See also ref.2.

DRUG DANGER UNDETECTED

The anti-inflammatory drug Ibufenac was marketed in Britain during 1966 but withdrawn two years later following 12 deaths, mainly through liver damage. Although submitted to "extensive" tests in mice, rats and dogs, no evidence of liver damage was detected except for a slight effect in rats exposed to lethal doses of the drug.[1]

Dr Cuthbert of the Medicine's Division at Britain's Department of Health and Social Security, explained that "Evidence of liver damage is sometimes detected in animal studies of non-steroidal anti-inflammatory drugs but usually no such evidence is forthcoming even in circumstances where a drug is eventually shown to be hepatotoxic [damaging to the liver] in man."[1]

Reference

1) M.F.Cuthbert in *Current Approaches in Toxicology*, Ed. B.Ballantyne (Wright & Sons, 1977).

TRAGEDY HITS HEPATITIS VICTIMS

In June 1993, researchers at America's National Institutes of Health abruptly halted trials of a new drug to combat hepatitis B virus, following deaths and serious complications among participants. Although the drug, fialuridine (FIAU), was intended to improve liver disease, many of the patients undergoing prolonged treatment were getting *worse* with several dying from liver failure.[1]

The liver toxicity surprised researchers, for the drug seemed safe and effective in animal experiments.[1] It reduced the amount of hepatitis virus in infected woodchucks, the "preferred" animal model, and was also tested for toxicity in mice, rats and rhesus monkeys. However, one of the trial's chief investigators later asked "...why didn't the animal toxicity studies show any abnormality at all due to the drug?"[2]

The metabolism of anti-viral drugs of this type is said to be very different in animals and people,[3] and the tragedy has prompted a closer look at related drugs to see if other patients are experiencing similar harmful effects.

References
1) N.Touchette, *The Journal of NIH Research*, 1993, 5, 33-35.
2) J.Hoofnagle, reported in ref.1.
3) C.Macilwain, *Nature*, 1993, July 22, 275.

LET'S LIBERATE SCIENCE

It is natural to ask why vivisection persists when there is always the risk of misleading predictions. In fact, there are powerful vested interests whose profits and livelihood depend on animal experiments. There are the drug and chemical companies who perform government-specified animal "safety" tests in order to market their products; the contract research laboratories who specialise in these procedures; the scientists who build their careers on animal experiments; and the animal breeders and cage and equipment suppliers who service the needs of university, government and industrial laboratories. Vivisection is big business.

The idea that animal tests are carried out to provide legal protection for the drug companies and political protection to the official government regulatory bodies, is fuelled by the fact that results sometimes appear to be conveniently ignored. In 1983, the British biochemist Dennis Parke wrote that "....corticosteroids are known to be teratogenic [producing birth defects] in rodents, the significance of which to man has never been fully understood, but nevertheless is assumed to be negligible. However, the practice of evaluating corticosteroid drugs in rodents still continues, and drugs which exhibit high levels of teratogenesis in rodents at doses similar to the human therapeutic dose are marketed, apparently as safe, with the manufacturer required only to state that the drug produces birth defects in experimental animals, the significance of which to man is unknown."[1]

As a consultant physician at London's Hammersmith Hospital pointed out, teratogenicity tests are "virtually useless scientifically" but do provide "some defence against public allegations of neglect of adequate drug testing. In other words 'something' is being done, although it is not the right thing."[2]

In the academic world, experiments on animals are ideally suited to the rapid production of scientific papers: researchers can produce results from a variety of species and then perform more experiments in an attempt to understand the differences! The laboratory rat has even been described as "an organism which, when injected, produces a paper."[3]

Animal research is also fast. With their shorter life-spans, laboratory animals have more rapidly-developing disease processes, again facilitating the rapid production of research papers.[4] This is vital in the "publish or perish" world of academic science where career advancement is primarily dependent on publications: the more articles published the better the chances of promotion and continued financial support.

It has become fashionable to study disease in the "controlled" environment of a laboratory, producing a further incentive to carry out animal experiments. Here, a disposable species can be manipulated as required and killed when convenient, providing experimenters with more freedom than their clinical counterparts who must do no harm to the people they study. The idea seems to have official approval since there is no shortage of funds for animal research. In the United States, the government's National Institutes of Health spends about twice as much on animal experiments as it does on research with human subjects.[5] (The fact that animal experiments are so readily funded is itself a major reason for its continuation.)

However, there is a price to be paid: animal models of human illness are artificial and cannot accurately reflect the situation in people. In contrast, clinical investigators know that whilst they may need more time and care to assimilate the necessary information, results will at least be directly relevant to human patients.

Another doctrine that pervades medical science and which influences the use of animals is that human findings must be replicated in the laboratory before finally being accepted. The policy can be disastrous as we have already seen with examples like smoking and asbestos. But the preference for animal experiments is so ingrained that even as late as 1964, the World Health Organisation was still recommending further animal testing of tobacco smoke despite overwhelming evidence for its effects in people.[6]

Ultimately, experimenters insist that animals must be used because the alternatives are inadequate. But these claims are immediately undermined by a simple fact: that when researchers are not able to use animals, they always manage to substitute other methods to achieve their objectives. Necessity becomes the mother of invention. For instance, although the use of animals to test the potency of vaccines is traditional, such an approach is of no value in assessing pneumonia vaccines because the causal organisms are generally not virulent for laboratory animals. As a result, scientists devised an alternative method based on chemical analysis and studies with human volunteers.[7]

Historically, a classic example is the conquest of yellow fever. In 1900 no animal was known to be susceptible, prompting studies with human volunteers which proved that mosquitoes did indeed transmit the disease.[8] These observations led to improved sanitation and quarantine measures in Havana where yellow fever, once rife, was eradicated.

Examples like this suggest that vivisection cannot be "essential" and could be eliminated if only scientists had the necessary motivation. However tradition exerts a powerful influence. Nothing better illustrates the mindset and lack of imagination that allows vivisection to flourish than the Draize Test. Shampoos, pesticides, weedkillers, ophthalmic agents, household detergents, even riot control gases, are applied to the eyes of conscious animals to measure irritancy. Rabbits are usually chosen but not for any scientific reason: they are simply cheap, readily-available, docile and have large eyes for assessing results. In fact the rabbit eye is a poor model for the human eye and the test has been repeatedly criticised in the scientific literature.[9]

It was eventually discovered that the traditional Draize Test, in which comparatively large doses are applied to rabbits' eyes, "has essentially no power to predict the results of accidental human eye exposure."[10] Although the test was introduced during World War II, little attempt had been made to develop a more humane and reliable alternative: toxicologists could only suggest using different species.

But if the Draize Test illustrates some of the worst aspects of scientific practice, it also shows how to combat vivisection. For it was during the 1980s, when animal protection groups focussed attention on the test, that attitudes started to change. Within a decade, 60 test-tube techniques were either in use or under development and some companies had stopped using rabbits.[11] In Britain, where the number of animal experiments is recorded annually, the use of rabbits in eye irritation tests declined from over 13,000 in 1980 to 3,242 by 1992.[12] Some rabbits are still used so there is no room for complacency but the campaign does show that public pressure, skillfully directed, can influence the procedures of science.

It would be nice to think that science could put its own house in order. Ideally, researchers would change their outlook and ask themselves a simple question before embarking on an experiment: how would I proceed if there were no animals? In reality, it will be an informed and determined public who finally provide the incentives for change. For all our sakes - Let's Liberate Science!

References

1) D.V.Parke in *Animals in Scientific Research: An Effective Substitute for Man?*, Ed. P.Turner (Macmillan, 1983)

2) P.Lewis in *Drugs and Pregnancy: Human Teratogenesis and Related Problems*, Ed. D.F.Hawkins (Churchill Livingstone, 1983)

3) A.R.Mitchell MD, *Lord Dowding Fund Bulletin*, 1981, No.16, 29-33.

4) *A Critical Look at Animal Research* (Medical Research Modernization Committee, New York, 1990).

5) *Alternatives to Animal Use in Research, Testing & Education*, US Congress, Office of Technology Assessment, 1986.

6) I.Tomatis et al, *Japanese Journal of Cancer Research*, 1989, vol.80, 795-807.

7) J.B.Robbins, *Journal of Infection*, 1979, vol.1, suppl.2, 61-72.

8) L.K.Altman, *Who Goes First? The Story of Self-Experimentation* (New York, Random House, 1987).

9) R.Sharpe, *Food & Chemical Toxicology*, 1985, vol.23, 139-143, and references therein.

10) F.E.Freeberg et al, *Fundamental & Applied Toxicology*, 1986, vol.7, 626-634.

11) C.G.Shayne in *Benchmarks: Alternative Methods in Toxicology*, Ed. M.A.Mehlman (Princeton Scientific Publishing Co.Inc., 1989).

12) Figures prior to 1987 may not be strictly comparable with later statistics owing to changes in the way the British government's Home Office classified animal experiments.

APPENDIX 1

Choice of Species

The examples highlighted in this book arise from physiological and biochemical differences between the species, making vivisection a fundamentally flawed concept. But difficulties are compounded because the choice of species so often depends on factors such as cost, breeding rate, litter size, ease of handling and tradition rather than anticipated similarity to people.[1]

For instance, by far the most commonly used animal is the mouse, representing almost 50% of the total![2] The *Introduction to Laboratory Animal Science & Technology* explains that "Their popularity lies in their prolific reproduction and comparative ease of management in domestication". Mice are also considerably cheaper than other animals and about half the cost of rats, their nearest rival in the number of animals used (see Appendix 2).

Rats and mice constitute the main species employed for testing the safety of drugs and other products (Appendix 2) yet it would be hard to find more "unreliable" animals. It is not even possible to accurately predict carcinogenicity in the mouse using data from rats.[3] Rodent toxicity tests are especially undermined by species differences in the speed and pattern of metabolism, or the way in which a substance is broken down by the body. If animals metabolize a drug more quickly than people, they are likely to miss harmful effects resulting from greater exposure. The Table shows how great these differences can be.[4]

Metabolism (in hours) of 4 drugs

	Rats	People
Phenylbutazone	6	72
Digitoxin	18	216
Digoxin	9	44
Hexobarbital	2.3	6

Animals will also miss side-effects if they metabolize the drug in a completely different way, not just at a different speed. In this case, one species might metabolize the drug into toxic fragments whilst another produces harmless by-products. A comparative study of 23 chemicals shows how serious the problem is: in only *four* cases did rats and people metabolize the product along the same biochemical pathway.[5]

Despite this, British figures show that rats are the main species used to study how drugs and other chemicals are distributed, metabolized and excreted by the body.[2] Furthermore, they are also the most commonly used animal in prolonged toxicity tests where differences in metabolism are likely to have the greatest effect.

The astonishing reliance on rodents prompted Edward Calabrese, Professor of Toxicology at the University of Massachusetts' School of Public Health, to state: "It seems almost incredible that the rat is the model so heavily relied upon when predicting human responses to toxic/carcinogenic agents. Whether the concern is absorption, tissue distribution, biliary excretion, intestinal flora, enterohepatic circulation, mechanisms of conjugation, and others, there are profound differences between the values of the rat and those of humans."[6] Calabrese is not opposed to animal experiments but lists such differences between rats and people as "... to make one ponder ... whether there is much predictive validity to this model".

Ironically, whilst rats are used to predict toxicity of drugs for human use, there is a major industry whose success depends on *differences* between the species! Companies marketing rodenticides hope to develop products that are toxic to rats but comparatively harmless to other animals and people. On the one hand, rats are expected to respond like human beings but in developing rodenticides it is assumed they are sufficiently different to enable highly specific poisons to be produced. For instance, researchers note that the raticide, Norbormide, "... is extremely lethal to a certain kind of rat, but not at all toxic to almost all other species known, including the subhuman primate and man. Indeed, if this were a drug and one based his evaluation of whether this compound was safe for man but not on the rat, it is doubtful whether such a drug would ever have been used for man".[7]

Rabbits are the main animal used for eye irritation tests but once again the reason is not scientific. The rabbit eye is a poor model for the human eye[8] but the Draize test traditionally relies on this species because it is cheap, readily available, easy to handle and has a large eye for assessing test results.[9] Primates are considered more relevant but, fortunately for them, drawbacks such as expense, availability and temperament have largely precluded their use for eye irritation tests. The rat too has been largely excluded, in part because it is not sufficiently docile.[6]

Choice of species also affects the study of disease. Rabbits are the most commonly used animal in atherosclerosis research despite substantial differences between the artificially induced condition and the naturally arising disorder in people. Whilst it is rare for lesions in rabbits to develop fibrosis, haemorrhage, ulceration and/or thrombosis, all of these are characteristic of the disease in human patients.[10] Pigs are considered the closest "model" for the condition in people but are regarded as expensive and difficult to work with. Rabbits have, therefore, become the species of choice since they are "easy to feed, care for and handle. They are readily available and inexpensive".[10]

Dogs are subjected to a bewildering variety of experiments, but if the scientific literature is any guide, most are used for cardiovascular research. Typically, scientists induce heart failure or other cardiac symptoms to test drugs or perform physiological experiments. However, the choice of dogs for heart research seems to have more to do with the convenience of working with these animals than any anticipated relevance to the human illness. For instance, they respond well to anaesthesia making them good subjects for the associated surgical interventions.[11] And most purpose-bred dogs are beagles, partly because of their docile temperament.[12]

In his book *Animal Models in Cardiovascular Research* (1985), Dr Gross notes that the use of dogs to assess treatments for ischemic heart disease - the most common cause of heart failure in people - is questionable because of differences in tissue injuries between the artificially induced animal model and the human clinical situation. Gross also states that "Overwhelmingly, the most used animal model for coronary circulation studies is the dog, despite evidence that the pig has a coronary vascular system more similar to that of man than does the dog". Nevertheless, pigs are still not a precise replica of the human condition.

Pro-vivisectionists often stress that most research uses rats and mice rather than, say, cats and dogs. The inference is that people will be less likely to object since rodents are not very popular amongst the public. But the tactic can backfire, for the heavy reliance on these animals is actually a very strong argument against the claim that vivisection is somehow "scientific". How could it be when the choice of species is so frequently dependent on non-scientific factors such as cost and convenience?

References

1) J. F. Dunne in *Textbook of Adverse Drug Reactions*, Ed. D. M. Davies (Oxford University Press, 1977).
2) *Statistics of Scientific Procedures on Living Animals, Great Britain, 1992* (HMSO, 1993).
3) F. J. Di Carlo, *Drug Metabolism Reviews*, 1984, vol. 15, 409-413.
4) R. Levine, *Pharmacology: Drug Actions & Reactions* (Little, Brown & Co., 1978).
5) R. L. Smith & J. Caldwell in *Drug Metabolism - From Microbe to Man*, Eds. D. V. Parke & R. L. Smith (Taylor & Francis, 1977).
6) E. J. Calabrese, *Principles of Animal Extrapolation* (Wiley & Sons, 1983).
7) F. Coulston & D. M. Serrone, *Annals of the New York Academy of Sciences*, 1969, vol. 162, 681-706.
8) See, for instance, E. V. Buehler & E. A. Newman *Toxicology & Applied Pharmacology*, 1964, vol. 6, 701-710; see also refs. 7 and 9.
9) B. Ballantyne & D. W. Swanston in *Current Approaches in Toxicology*, Ed. B. Ballantyne (John Wright, 1977).
10) D. R. Gross, *Animal Models in Cardiovascular Research* (Martinus Nijhoff, 1985).
11) C. J. Green, *Animal Anaesthesia* (Laboratory Animals Ltd., 1979).
12) C. Holden, *Science*, 1989, July 14, 124-125.

APPENDIX 2

Species Used

Some idea of the main species used in experiments "... likely to cause ... pain, suffering, distress or lasting harm ... ", can be obtained from detailed British figures.

Table A : All Experiments

Species	No. of Animals in 1992	% of Total
Mice	1,448,960	49.5
Rats	833,004	28.4
Guinea Pigs	106,934	3.6
Hamsters	13,269	0.45
Gerbils	10,157	0.35
Rabbits	79,450	2.7
Cats	3,692	0.1
Dogs	9,085*	0.3
Ferrets	4,062	0.14
Horses, Donkeys or Crossbreeds	1,492	0.05
Pigs	6,581	0.2
Sheep	18,310	0.6
Cattle	6,794	0.2
Monkeys	5,018	0.17
Birds	220,312	7.5
Amphibians	18,938	0.6
Fish	138,251	4.7
Others	3,949	0.13
Total	2,928,258	

* 8,723 were beagles, 65 greyhounds
Source: *Statistics of Scientific Procedures on Living Animals, Great Britain 1992* (HMSO, 1993).

Table B : Species used in Safety Tests*

Main species	Short test duration (days/wks)		Prolonged duration (months/yrs)		Skin irritancy		Eye irritancy		Birth defects/ mutagens	
Mice	196,755	(54%)	18,731	(17%)	2,771	(13.5%)	-		12,985	(33%)
Rats	67,530	(18.5%)	72,478	(66%)	910	(4.4%)	110	(3.3%)	21,311	(54%)
Other Rodents	8,892	(2.4%)	883	(0.8%)	9,673	(47%)	-		268	(0.7%)
Rabbits	31,903	(8.7%)	469	(0.4%)	7,126	(34.7%)	3,242	(96%)	5,006	(12.6%)
Dogs	1,945	(0.5%)	1,881	(1.7%)	-		-		-	
Monkeys	770	(0.2%)	1,029	(0.9%)	-		4	(0.12%)	-	
Ungulates	747	(0.2%)	-		47	(0.2%)	13	(0.4%)	-	
Birds	6,442	(1.8%)	3,979	(3.6%)	-		-		-	
Fish	49,677	(13.6%)	10,611	(9.6%)	-		-		28	(0.07%)
All Species	364,790	(100%)	110,061	(100%)	20,527	(100%)	3,369	(100%)	39,598	(100%)

*   Products tested include drugs and medical appliances, agricultural chemicals, industrial substances, environmental pollutants, household products, food additives, and cosmetics and toiletries.

Source: *Statistics of Scientific Procedures on Living Animals, Great Britain, 1992* (HMSO, 1993).

ORGANISATIONS
(space precludes the listing of every campaigning group)
UK:
Animal Aid
The Old Chapel, Bradford Street, Tonbridge TN9 1AW Kent
T: 0742 364546
F: 0742 366533
Advocates for Animals
10 Queensferry Street, Edinburgh EH2 4PG Scotland
T: 031 225 6039
F: 031 220 6377
British Union for the Abolition of Vivisection (BUAV)
16a Crane Grove, Islington N7 8LB London
T: 071 700 4888
F: 071 700 0252
Animal Concern
62 Old Dumbarton Rd, Glasgow G3 8RG Scotland
T: 041 334 6014
F: 041 445 6470

USA:
American Anti-Vivisection Society (AAVS)
801 Old York Rd #204, Jenkintown PA 19046-1685
T: 215 887 0816
F: 215 887 2088
Association of Veterinarians for Animal Rights (AVAR)
PO Box 6269, Vacaville CA 95696
T: 707 451 1391
F: 707 449 8775
Medical Research Modernization Committee (MRMC)
PO Box 2751 Grand Central Station, New York NY 10163-2751
T: 1 212 876 1368
F: none
National Anti-Vivisection Society (NAVS)
53 W.Jackson Blvd.#1552, Chicago IL 60604
T: 312 427 6065
F: 312 427 6524

New England Anti-Vivisection Society (NEAVS)
333 Washington Street #850, Boston MA 02108
T: 617 523 6020
F: 617 523 7925
People for the Ethical Treatment of Animals (PETA)
PO Box 42516, Washington DC 20015-0516
T: 301 770 7444 / 203 866 5223
F: 301 770 8969
Physicians Committee for Responsible Medicine (PCRM)
PO Box 6322, Washington DC 20015
T: 202 686 2210
F: 202 686 2216

WORLDWIDE:
International Association Against Painful Experiments on Animals (IAAPEA)
PO Box 215, St.Albans AL3 4RD Hertfordshire England
T: 0727 835386
F: 0727 864356
The IAAPEA has 52 member societies operating in 29 countries and has consultative status with the United Nations Economic & Social Council.

FURTHER READING

The Cruel Deception - the use of animals in medical research
Dr Robert Sharpe (Thorsons, 1988)

Animal Experimentation: The Consensus Changes
Ed. Dr Gill Langley (Macmillan Press, 1989)

Animal Liberation (Second edition) Peter Singer (Thorsons, 1990)

The Case for Animal Rights, Tom Regan (Routledge & Kegan
Paul, 1984)

INDEX

Barbiturates, 121
Benoxaprofen, 120
Beta-blockers, 73
Benzene, 13, 25
Benzodiazepines, 74
Birth defects, 65, 67-68, 79, 83-84, 134, 145
Bleach, 125
Bradykinin, 30
Brain research, 30, 97
Brij 35, 87
Brij 58, 87
Butadiene, 39
Butazolidine, *see phenylbutazone.*

Cambridge University, 17
Cancer
       anti-cancer drugs, 63, 64, 69, 72, 76-77, 107, 112
       cancer-causing agents, 13, 21, 24, 25, 33, 79, 83-84, 106, 109,
       117-118, 126-127, 128-129
       carcinogenicity tests, 13, 24, 25, 35, 39, 76-77, 102, 104, 106
       111, 122, 126-127, 128-129, 136, 139-140
       prevention, 76-77, 111, 117 - 118
       toxicity of treatment, 88
Cancer Research Campaign, 126
Carbenoxalone, 70
Cataract, 26, 28, 99
Chemie Grünenthal, 67
Childbed fever, 119
Chloramphenicol, 37
Chloroform, 59-60
Chymotrypsin, 26
Ciba-Geigy, 34
Cirrhosis, 21
Clindamycin, 71
Clioquinol, 34
Clonidine, 31
Coal, 40-41, 117
Coconut soap, 52
Contraception, 35, 75, 107-108
Cortisone, 78, 112
Cosmetic ingredients, 52, 55

CS, 101
Coumarin, 103
Cyclosporin, 17, 75, 91, 130-131
Cystic fibrosis, 15

Deadly nightshade, 11
Dental caries, 102
Depoprovera, 107-108
Dermatitis, 42
DES, 83-84
Detergents, 52,87
Dichlorvos, 11
Diet studies, 111, 117
Digitalis, 85
Digoxin, 85
Dinitrophenol, 28
Dipterex, 23
Disinfectants, 11
Dista, 120
Distillers Company, 67
Domperidone, 54
Draize eye test, *see eye irritancy tests.*
Draize skin test, *see skin irritancy tests.*
Drug dependence, 74, 75, 86
Drug research, 30
Drugs,
> anaemia, 61
> antibiotic, 37, 71, 116
> anticancer, *see Cancer.*
> antidepressant, 44, 66, 92
> antidiarrhoeal, 34
> anti-emetic, 54
> antifungal, 96
> anti-inflammatory, 20, 47, 58, 95, 110, 120, 132
> antitubercular, 66, 75
> anti-ulcer, 70, 122
> antiviral, 113-115, 133
> asthma, 32, 94
> blood pressure, 31, 73
> cholesterol lowering, 28
> cough & cold, 50, 93
> diuretic, 48, 90
> epileptic, 105
> fertility, 76-77

heart, 49, 56, 73, 85, 98, 123
obesity, 28, 82
ophthalmic, 26, 51, 57, 99
pain killing, 19, 31, 33, 53, 110
parasitic, 27
reproductive, 83-84
tranquillizing, 74
transplant, 17, 75, 91, 130-131
veterinary, 11-12
withdrawn or restricted, 20, 28, 32, 34, 37, 48, 49, 54, 56, 58, 66, 67-68, 82, 92, 98, 120, 132

Dupanol, 87

Eczema, 42
Eli Lilly, 120
Encainide, 123
Enterovioform, *see Clioquinol.*
Epilepsy, 105
Eraldin, *see Practolol.*
Erythromycin, 116
Ethanol, *see Alcohol.*
Eye irritancy tests, 26, 27, 50, 51, 87, 101, 136-137, 141, 145
Evicromil, 94

Fats, 111
Fenclozic acid, 95
Fertility, 76
Fialuridine, 133
Fibre, 111
FK506, 17
Flecainide, 123
Fluoridation, 102
Food additive, 103
Food deprivation experiments, 97
Formaldehyde, 104
Furmethide, 57
Furosemide, 90

Genetic Engineering, 14-15
Glass fibre, 106
Glaucoma, 57, 99
Glaxo, 122

Halothane, 38
Haloxon, 11
Heart,
>drugs, *see Drugs.*
>research, 30, 142
>transplants, 91, 130-131
>valves, 45-46

Hepatitis B, 133
HIV, 15, 89
Human cell tests, 12, 30, 44, 58, 72, 75, 85, 114-115
Hygiene, 119

Ibufenac, 132
Ibuprofen, 110
Imperial Cancer Research Fund, 76-77
ICI, 73, 76-77, 95, 98
Inflammation, 30
Inhalation tests, 100, 106
Institute of Psychiatry, 105
Iproniazid, 66
Iron, 61
Iron Sorbitol, 61
Isoprenaline, 32
Isopropyl myristate, 52

Ketoconazole, 96

Lemon juice, 52
Lethal poisoning tests (LD50), 110
Leukemia, 18, 25, 37, 72, 112
Leukotrienes, 30
Librium, 22, 74
Lindane, 27
LSD, 11

Malaria, 43
Menthol, 50
Methanol, 80
Mer-29, *see Triparanol.*
Methysergide, 19

Mexaform, *see Clioquinol.*
Mianserin, 44
Miners, 40-41, 100
Mitoxantrone, 69
Mitral valves, 45-46
Morphine, 53

National Cancer Institute, 24, 72, 112
National Institutes of Health, 12, 135
Nickel, 42
Nizoral, *see ketoconazole.*
NSAIDs, *see Drugs, anti-inflammatory.*
Nuclear industry, 18
NutraSweet Company, 105

Olive oil, 124
Omeprazole, 122
Oncomouse, 15
Opren, 120
Oraflex, 120
Organophosphates, 23
Overdose, 110
Oxyphenbutazone, 58
Oxytetracycline, 116

Penicillin, 116
Perhexiline, 49
Pesticides, 23, 141
Pethidine, 86
Pfizer, 13
Pharmacology, *see Drug research.*
Phenacetin, 33
Phenylbutazone, 58
Pine oil cleaner, 52
Pneumoconiosis, 40-41
Pneumonia, 136
Polio, 113-115
Practolol, 98
Prednisone, 112
Prenylamine, 56

Proctor & Gamble, 52
Pronethalol, 73
Propranolol, 73
Prostaglandins, 30
Psicofuranine, 63
Puerperal fever, 119

Radiation, 18, 79
Ranitidine, 122
Richardson Merrell, 49
Rifampicin, 75
Riot control gases, 101
Roussel Laboratories, 47
Rubber, manufacture of, 39

Selacryn, 48
Sellafield, 18
Selsun, 51
Shampoos, 51
Shock, septic, 29
Silica, 40-41, 109
Silicosis, 109
Skin irritancy tests, 42, 52, 55, 101, 124, 125, 145
SMON, 34
Smoking & lung cancer, 13, 118, 126-127, 136
Sodium monensin, 11
Soap, 52
Soot, 13
Sparsomycin, 64
Spinal cord injury, 62
Squalene, 55
Starvation, 97
Steroids, 29, 43, 62, 65, 78, 99, 134
Stroke, 121
Suprofen, 20
Suprol, *see Suprofen.*
Surgam, 47

Talc, 100
Tamoxifen, 76-77
Tanderil, *see oxyphenbutazone.*
Thalidomide, 67-68
Tobacco, *see smoking.*
Transplants, 17, 75, 91, 130-131
Tranquillizers, 74
Transgenic animals, 15
Triparanol, 28
Tuberculosis, 12, 75

Vaccine research, 89, 113-115, 136
Valium, 74
Viruses, 89, 113-115, 118
Vitamin C, 12

Wallernberg syndrome type 1, 15
Warner Lambert, 52
Water treatment, 102
Wellcome Research Laboratory, 86
Wellcome Trust, 105
World Health Organisation, 44, 136

X-rays, 79

Yellow fever, 136
Yellow star thistle, 11

Zantac, see ranitidine.
Zelmid, *see zimelidine.*
Zimelidine, 92
Zipeprol, 93